The
HIGH LEVEL BRIDG
and
NEWCASTLE CENTRAL STATION

Published 1999 for the
High Level Bridge and Central Station 150 Committee

Published by the North Eastern Railway Association

on behalf of the

High Level Bridge and Central Station 150 Committee

August 1999

ISBN 1 873513 28 3 (softback)
ISBN 1 873513 29 1 (hardback)

Contents

Acknowledgements

In addition to those mentioned in the Preface the authors particularly wish to thank John Mallon for sorting out the complexities of Newcastle's signalling history for Chapter 7 and providing much valuable information for other chapters of the book. Peter Elliston has given a brief account, from his extensive research, of the unique piece of track work that linked the High Level Bridge to Central Station, namely the east end diamonds. Dr Ian Robert's appendix on Ridsdale iron has sorted out the facts from the legends about the local iron used in the High Level Bridge. Dr R. W. Rennison kindly allowed the authors to draw freely from his 1980 Newcomen Society paper on the High Level Bridge which presented invaluable references to the early schemes to bridge the Tyne and on the construction of the bridge itself. The recent maintenance history of the bridge was covered in Bill Preston's 1987 paper to the Institution of Civil Engineers and he has generously allowed it to be used.

The following have also been most helpful in providing information and material: Carol Arrowsmith (I.C.E. Archivist), Philip Atkins (N.R.M. Librarian), Roger Bastin, Alan Blower, Alan Bowman, Ian S. Carr, Malcolm Charlton, John Crompton (National Museums of Scotland), Chris Emerson, John Fleming, Andrew Greg and Ruth Trotter (Laing Art Gallery, Newcastle), June Holmes and the Natural History Society of Northumbria, John Ives (formerly of British Rail's Architecture and Design Group), Hugh Murray, Les Paul, Conrad Pointon (Railtrack Records Centre), D. J. Williamson, Ann Wilson (Ken Hoole Study Centre), also the staff of the British Library (Thorp Arch), Local Studies Section of Newcastle Central Library, Mitchell Library (Glasgow), Northumberland County Records Office and Tyne and Wear Archives.

Special thanks must go to Peter Bryant, of Pickering, for turning over 100 pages of J.F.A.'s illegible scrawl into a perfectly ordered typescript and for formatting the remainder of the book.

The information contained in this volume has been gleaned from primary sources and has been specifically checked where it differs from opinions contained in print elsewhere.

J.F.A. & W.F.

Preface

High Level Bridge – 150 – Central Station

As chairman of "The High Level Bridge and Central Station 150 Committee" it is my privilege to write the preface for this book.

The committee was formed to organise recognition of the 150th anniversaries of the High Level Bridge and Central Station in 1999 and 2000 respectively. Membership of the committee comes from railway and historical societies and representatives from the Gateshead and Newcastle local authorities. My thanks go to everyone who has attended and contributed to its work.

The High Level Bridge was built under the supervision of Robert Stephenson and the rail deck was opened by Queen Victoria on 28 September 1849. This completed a direct route along the east coast to Scotland. The bridge is a magnificent historic feature on Tyneside with the rail and road decks still in heavy daily use.

The Central Station was designed by the famous Tyneside architect John Dobson and was opened by Queen Victoria on 29 August 1850. It remains a tribute to our forebears that the station and its services have responded to changes over the years and maintained its important role in the transport systems of the area. These changes include the introduction of a pioneering electrification scheme for the Tyneside local services, as early as 1904, and more recently for the local rapid transit Metro system and the national GNER services between England and Scotland.

Details of all this, and more, are included in the authoritative chapters of this book which include maps, drawings and photographs covering the origins of railways and the related architecture in Gateshead and Newcastle from 1845 to the present day.

Most importantly the book is a lasting recognition of the importance to the region, and beyond, of the pioneering work of influential men like Thomas Harrison, Robert Stephenson, John Dobson and George Hudson.

The production of the book has been made possible by two groups of people; the authors and our financial supporters.

Thanks must therefore be paid to John Addyman and Bill Fawcett (North Eastern Railway Association) for their joint authorship, knowledge and network of willing co-contributors; Eileen Carnaffin (Gateshead Library) and Vicky Haworth (Robert Stephenson Trust) who have both readily provided historical evidence together with Tony Cormack (North Eastern Railway Association) who has also arranged the printing. As ever, there are others too numerous to mention here and my thanks also goes to them.

Without support from the local authorities in Gateshead and Newcastle, the societies represented on the committee and a number of individuals, the production of this book would not have taken place. On behalf of the committee and the readers I therefore say a sincere thank you to those who have provided financial backing. Details of all the contributing groups and their contact addresses appear elsewhere in the book.

Finally, I thank my wife and family for their support and understanding as I resigned from one voluntary post only to take up the challenge of chairing the 150 Committee!

KEITH STEWART
Chairman
High Level Bridge and Central Station 150 Committee
Newcastle Upon Tyne
May 1999

Colour Plate I   The Tyne Bridges. From the bottom: The Tyne Bridge 1928; Swing-bridge 1876; High Level Bridge 1849; Queen Elizabeth II Bridge (Metro) 1981; King Edward VII Bridge 1906 and the new Redheugh Bridge 1984. Central Station is top right, while bottom right is the viaduct leading to Manors. Les Paul.

Colour Plate II   Central Station viewed during the construction of the underground Metro station. This entailed the temporary dismantling of a corner of the portico after tunnelling led to subsidence. Beyond the three spans of the original roof can be seen the 1959 signalbox which bridged the rear of the station and has just been removed during the winter of 1998-9. Les Paul.

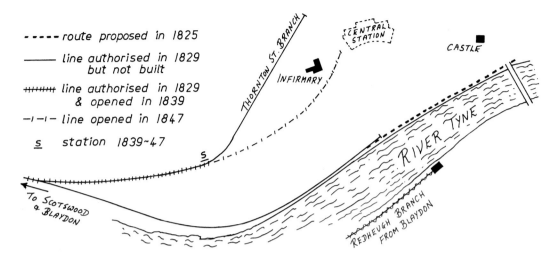

Fig. 1.1   The Newcastle & Carlisle Railway's projected and actual routes into Newcastle.   Bill Fawcett.

Plate 1.1   Redheugh Station - opened 1 March 1837 - the first passenger station to serve Gateshead and Newcastle, depicted by John Wilson Carmichael. To the right of the temporary passenger shed can be glimpsed the funnel of a steamer which conveyed passengers across the Tyne to a Newcastle 'station' in the Close. In front, Carmichael has shown wagons standing at the foot of the Brandling Junction Railway's Redheugh Incline, which opened in January 1839. Robert Mylne's Tyne Bridge, on the site of the present Swing Bridge, features prominently, as does the Newcastle Infirmary, the white building at extreme left.   Bill Fawcett collection.

Chapter 1

MAIN LINES TO THE TYNE

BILL FAWCETT

Overview

Northumberland and Durham are widely regarded as the cradle of railways, so it is fitting that they should have been united by so striking a monument as Robert Stephenson's High Level Bridge, bearing the East Coast Main Line from London to Edinburgh. Yet, seen in the context of the furious pace of railway development during the eighteen-thirties and forties, the main line was relatively late in coming to Tyneside.

The recorded history of waggonways extends back four centuries[1] and by 1800 the banks of the Tyne were well served by horse-operated lines conveying coal for shipment - much of it destined for the coastal trade to London[2]. The Stockton & Darlington Railway, opened in September 1825, was intended to open up collieries west of Bishop Auckland, and passengers and merchandise were carried by a variety of small operators using horse traction - the company's locomotives being reserved for the coal trains. The first public railway in a recognisably modern sense, employing locomotives for the haulage of all its traffic and providing stations and goods warehouses, was the Liverpool & Manchester, which opened in September 1830. This was followed by a surge of development, most significantly that of the London & Birmingham Railway in whose construction Robert Stephenson first assumed the dominant role in the partnership with his father.

The London & Birmingham opened in stages between July 1837 and April 1838, and for a dozen years, until the completion of the Great Northern Railway, its Euston Square terminus formed the only gateway for travel to the Midlands and North of England. The completion of the Midland Counties, North Midland and York & North Midland Railways brought the main line to York in 1840, followed by the Great North of England Railway (the first GNER) extension to Darlington in January 1841. Shortage of money halted the GNER's planned continuation to Newcastle but George Hudson, a York entrepreneur who achieved fame as the first Railway King, organised a Newcastle & Darlington Junction Railway (N&DJ) which opened to an elegant terminus in Greene's Field, Gateshead, in June 1844.

Hudson followed up by promoting a Newcastle & Berwick Railway (N&B), a satellite of the N&DJ with which it jointly undertook the expense of building the High Level Bridge across the River Tyne. Meanwhile the North British Railway was advancing down from Edinburgh and opened to Berwick in June 1846. The following March the first two sections of the N&B opened, from Chathill to Tweedmouth and Newcastle (Heaton Junction) to Morpeth, with the intervening stretch opening on 1 July 1847 albeit with temporary wooden viaducts across the rivers Blyth, Wansbeck, Coquet and Aln. Main line trains at last began crossing the Tyne on another temporary viaduct in August 1848 followed by one across the Tweed in October, thus completing the route from Euston to Edinburgh.

To mark the completion of the final links in this chain, Queen Victoria and Prince Albert performed a series of ceremonial openings in the course of journeys to and from their summer holidays on Deeside. Heading south, on 28 September 1849, Victoria formally opened the High Level Bridge, which had come into use six weeks earlier. Heading north the following year on 29 August, they opened Newcastle Central Station, though it was still incomplete, followed by the Royal Border Bridge at Berwick, which had already been brought into traffic.

The Newcastle & Carlisle Railway - the first public railway on Tyneside

The first public railway to be constructed in the area was the Newcastle & Carlisle (N&C), which received an Act of Parliament in May 1829 authorising the company to build a line from the Newcastle riverside at the west end of the Close, just west of the present King Edward Bridge, to the basin of the canal linking Carlisle with the Solway Firth. The first serious investment in transport on this route had been the construction of the Military Road, following the Jacobite conflict of 1745-6. For much of its length the road kept to high ground alongside the Roman Wall, doing little to serve the valley communities, whose needs were addressed instead by a variety of canal schemes. None of these came to anything but extensive surveys were carried out. A serious drawback was that the Tyne itself could not readily be improved for navigation beyond its tidal limit, just above Blaydon.

Colour Plate III   T. E. Harrison's office copy of the first edition 25 inch/mile O.S. map of 1857, reproduced full-size. This was retained as the NER's key map after his death, and was updated to show planned developments. Thus the original YNB engine sheds at the rear of Central station can still be seen in grey under the brown of the 1893 island platform, with the N&C engine shed also showing through at the west end. The diversion of Forth Street on to a new alignment, to accommodate the 1890-4 station enlargements is shown in brown. At the north end of the High Level Bridge can be seen the additional curve proposed in 1890 but soon dropped. The Forth Goods Station and King Edward Bridge have been added, but the map also reveals Harrison's original proposal for a west-end crossing - rubbed out on the original document but reinstated here as a broken line - with its curve to avoid the Forth Goods. The goods department employed many horses, and their stables are shown in two locations south of Pottery Lane. Gateshead Locomotive Works is shown with only the first stage of its large engine shed completed.

The ingenuity of the canal promoters is shown by a plan prepared by the engineer William Chapman (1779-1867), showing a canal without locks, running along the contour from the Tyne at Haydon Bridge to the Town Moor at Newcastle, access to the river there being through an inclined plane in the vicinity of Benwell[3].

The railway scheme was surveyed under the direction of Benjamin Thompson, a colliery owner with extensive experience of laying waggonways and a strong prejudice in favour of stationary engines and rope haulage rather than locomotives, which he had found to be unreliable. A first application was made to Parliament in the session 1825-6 but withdrawn on account of errors in the survey. Delay then ensued while the promoters negotiated with the Earl of Carlisle who objected both to their route and the prospect of competition with his own waggonway, carrying coal to the city of Carlisle.

Like many early railways the N&C was principally concerned with coal, mineral and merchandise traffic rather than passengers. This was evident at Newcastle, where the route projected in 1825 would have carried the railway along the riverside on a new quay to the north end of the Tyne Bridge, with a siding extending through one arch to serve the Quayside[4]. The line authorised in 1829 stopped further west, at the Skinner Burn, and included a branch leaving the main line near Elswick and climbing steeply up the hillside to Thornton Street, just off Westgate Road (Fig. 1.3), to serve the upper part of the town. This had been opposed by John Hodgson, owner of the Elswick Estate and residing at Elswick Hall, so Parliament gave him a veto, making construction of the branch conditional on his consent.

The quayside terminus was an awkward compromise, sited above the Tyne Bridge which was navigable by keels, small boats used to carry coal downriver, but not by sea-going vessels. In January 1830 a letter in a local newspaper[5] advocated a south bank route terminating in Gateshead downstream of the bridge. In the event, the east end of the line took a totally different form, shaped by developments within Newcastle and the arrival of other railways. That it could evolve was due to the lengthy timescale for the construction of the approximately sixty mile route. To ease their finances the company began with the most productive stretches of line, at the Carlisle end and from Hexham to Blaydon, which provided a shipping point on the Tyne. To oversee the work they engaged Francis Giles (c1787-1847), an experienced civil engineer with expertise in harbour works but little knowledge of railways.

Giles was an able bridge designer, as his viaducts at the west end of the railway amply testify, but there was friction with the directors, concerned at the slow progress of the works and infrequency of his visits. A further handicap was the reluctance of many shareholders to pay their calls (the share price was demanded in instalments as needed) and the company had to borrow extensively from the Exchequer Loan Board. Matters came to a head in the Spring of 1833 and in June Giles was relegated to a nominal role as consulting engineer, the works being carried out by his resident engineer John Blackmore under the supervision of a Committee of Management experienced in the construction and operation of colliery lines, namely Benjamin Thompson, Nicholas Wood and George Johnson[6].

Almost six years from the passing of the Act, the first section of the railway, a mere 17 miles from Hexham to Blaydon, was formally opened on 9 March 1835; regular traffic commencing the next day. No works had been carried out further east and passengers continued their journey to Newcastle either by horse-drawn omnibus over the recently-built Scotswood Chain Bridge[7] or by steam boat. Further openings followed rapidly: Hexham to Haydon Bridge on 28 June 1836, Greenhead to Carlisle (London Road) on 19 July 1836, the extension to the Carlisle Canal on 9 March 1837 and, at last, the gap having been filled between Haydon Bridge and Greenhead, the grand opening took place on 18 June 1838. The Carlisle trains now ran from a terminus at Askew's Quay, in Gateshead, and to see how this had come about we must explore the other railway schemes in the area.

Urban Development in the Eighteen-Thirties

Before considering other railways promoted in Newcastle and Gateshead during the eighteen-thirties, it is important to establish the situation of the two towns. Newcastle and Gateshead grew up on the line of a bridge built by the Roman Army at a point where the Tyne becomes hemmed in by steep hillsides on both banks. For centuries they were linked by a medieval bridge, its ownership split between Newcastle Corporation and the Bishop of Durham and bearing houses which gave it a picturesque resemblance to the old London Bridge. Like many others it was severely damaged in the great flood of 1771 and its temporary successor was replaced by a new bridge to the design of Robert Mylne (1733-1811), which remained in use until 1866 before being demolished to clear the way for construction of the present swing bridge[8].

Mylne's handsome nine-arched bridge had two big disadvantages. Its arches were a hindrance to navigation and the road approaches on both banks were inconveniently steep for horse-drawn traffic, a problem aggravated as both towns spread further away from their riverside origins across the plateaux high above. To improve access to the upper towns a number of schemes were put forward for supplementary or replacement bridges, although nothing was done until the construction of the High Level Bridge, other than the widening of Mylne's bridge, begun in 1801[9]. A comprehensive account of these proposals has been published by R.W. Rennison[10], a list from which is reproduced in Appendix 1, so only two of the early ones will be mentioned here, both distinguished by an ingenious avoidance of the costly and lengthy construction of river piers.

In 1826, before work began on his Scotswood Bridge, Captain Samuel Brown had proposed a suspension bridge spanning the Tyne at a height of approximately 100 feet, between Greene's Field in Gateshead and the Back Row in Newcastle, an alignment upstream of the present High Level Bridge and at a comparable level. Two years later the distinguished Edinburgh civil engineer and lighthouse designer Robert Stevenson suggested the first double-decker scheme, based on Mylne's bridge. A fine model in the Royal Scottish Museum (Colour Plate IV) shows masonry piers centred on those of the existing bridge, which was to be retained, and carrying cast-iron arches bearing a roadway approximately 75 feet above the river[10]. The carriageway would have been transferred to the upper level, albeit restricted to Mylne's original width of 21 feet 6 inches. Footways would have remained along either side of the old bridge, with arches in the centre of Stevenson's piers apparently providing a route for horses. Criticisms of a later proposal[11] suggest that Mylne's piers might not have been adequate to bear the considerably increased load.

Fig. 1.2   Central Gateshead on the eve of expansion, mapped in Thomas Oliver's 1830 survey of Newcastle
& Gateshead. Note the concentration of development along the riverbank in Pipewellgate and Hillgate.
Gateshead Central Library.

FIRST PROPOSAL FOR A HIGH LEVEL BRIDGE FOR NEWCASTLE-ON-TYNE MADE IN THE YEAR 1828 FOR THE CORPORATION OF NEWCASTLE.
BY ROBERT STEVENSON, F.R.S.E., F.G.S., CIVIL ENGINEER, EDINBURGH.
PRESENTED BY MESSRS D. & T. STEVENSON.

Colour Plate IV   Robert Stevenson's model of his 1828 proposal for a high-level road bridge linking Newcastle and Gateshead and built on top of Robert Mylne's Tyne Bridge. Reproduced by permission of the Trustees of the National Museums of Scotland.

Colour Plate V   A bridge under the long-abandoned Redheugh Incline, where it passes under the south-western approach to Charles Harrison's King Edward Bridge. The Redheugh Station lay on the river bank a short distance upstream. This underbridge may have begun life with a wooden deck similar to that shown further down the line in Carmichael's engraving (Plate 1.1).

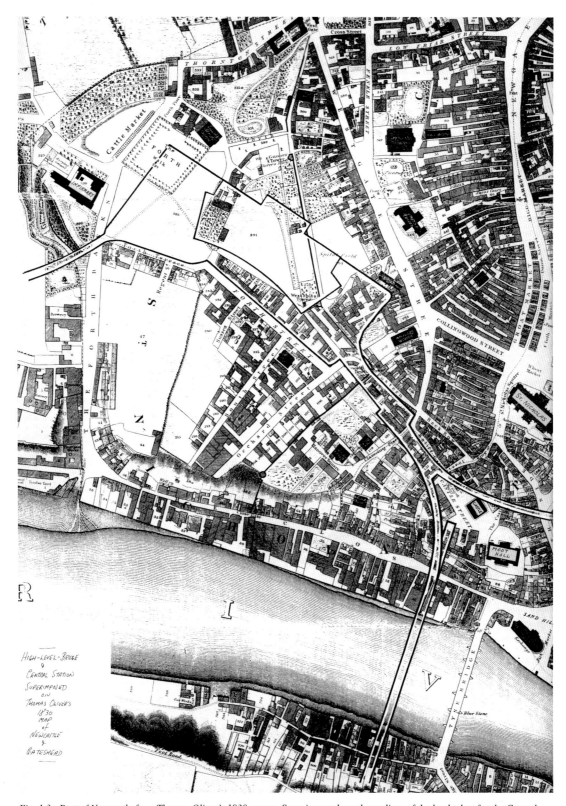

Fig. 1.3   Part of Newcastle from Thomas Oliver's 1830 survey. Superimposed are the outlines of the land taken for the Central Station, High Level Bridge and approaches.   Gateshead Central Library

Thomas Oliver's detailed plan of 1830 (Figs. 1.2 and 1.3) gives a vivid picture of both towns on the eve of hectic expansion. Much of Newcastle was still confined within the lines of its medieval walls, although development was spreading out along Westgate Road and to the north, in the vicinity of Barras Bridge. Even within the walls there remained the huge open space of the Nun's Field and the gardens and mansion house of Anderson Place, today covered by Grey and Grainger Streets. Gateshead was confined to the riverside and development along the High Street and Oakwellgate; West Street was the boundary of the urban area, with open fields occupying its west side.

Newcastle's transformation was carried out by a visionary builder and developer, Richard Grainger (1797-1861), aided by the long-serving town clerk John Clayton[12], in generally close co-operation with the Corporation, and inspired by Edinburgh's New Town and John Nash's Regent Street[13]. Grainger's developments began in 1819 with the typical Georgian brick terrace of Higham Place but soon moved to a grander scale with the sandstone facades of Eldon Square, Greek-Revival begun in 1825, and the even more stylish Leazes Terrace, begun in 1829. By the end of the eighteen-thirties Grainger had constructed a new and elegant town centre, unified by neo-classical frontages that extended across entire blocks, and dignified by public buildings which included the Grainger Markets, Theatre Royal and Royal Arcade. This made the Newcastle & Carlisle Railway's proposals for a main line terminating by the river seem increasingly inappropriate; it also created a climate of expectation which strongly influenced the ultimate design of Newcastle Central Station.

The advantageous siting of Central Station close to the city centre was made possible by the survival of unbuilt land to the west, astride the town wall, notably the two areas of the Forth and Spital[14]. The Forth (clearly seen in Fig. 1.3) was an area of 11 acres outside the wall, belonging to the town and long used for the recreation of its citizens. In the second half of the seventeenth century it was laid out with a bowling green, surrounded by a double avenue of lime trees and with a balconied tavern along the north side. Described by Mackenzie in 1827 as 'the most convenient and delightful promenade in the vicinity of the town' it was also a popular venue for demonstrations and witnessed a serious encounter during the Chartist fervour of Summer 1839, when cavalry were brought from Fenham Barracks to scatter the protesters, yet it disappeared peaceably under Neville Street and the station. The Spital Field lay just inside the town wall and took its name from the Hospital of the Blessed Virgin Mary, a medieval foundation in the patronage of the Corporation which survived Henry VIII's Dissolutions to become the home of the Grammar School and remain a venue for civic events. The Virgin Mary trustees, nominated by the Corporation, held extensive lands in this area and were able, with the Corporation, to facilitate not only the construction of the original station but its enlargement forty years later.

The Struggle for the Tyne

In 1833, with construction proceeding between Hexham and Blaydon, the Newcastle & Carlisle Railway reconsidered the continuation of its line to the east. Already there had been two schemes for railways from Blaydon to Gateshead, one extending to South Shields and Monkwearmouth, and though neither came to anything the company could not afford to leave the route open for others to occupy. The directors therefore chose to defer building their line into Newcastle and instead promote an extension along the south bank of the river to a deepwater berth at Hebburn Quay. Given their difficulties in raising capital, they set up a separate company, the Blaydon, Gateshead & Hebburn Railway (BGH), in which N&C shareholders were encouraged to invest. Thomas Sopwith was engaged to survey the route, with John Blackmore as engineer, and an Act of Parliament was obtained on 22 May 1834.

The BGH was intended to continue along the river bank as far as Redheugh, on the west side of Gateshead, then turn south east and climb the hillside by an incline at about 1 in 15, before levelling out and heading into a tunnel approximately 550 yards long under West Street and High Street. It was then to keep to the edge of the high ground before descending another incline to Hebburn Quay. A number of branches were planned, including one from the foot of the Redheugh Incline along the riverside to Pipewellgate[15]. Apart from the tunnel, the engineering works were modest and the line should have been constructed quite rapidly. Things were not that simple, however. The N&C saw the possibility of making a low-level bridge directly from the BGH into Newcastle, and the Act therefore gave them a right, if they chose, to make that portion of the line between Blaydon and any such crossing.

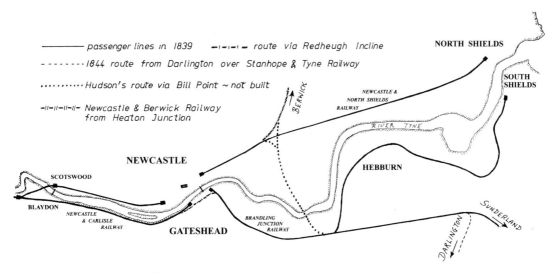

Fig. 1.4 *Tyneside Passenger Railways in 1839, showing also the connections subsequently made to form the East Coast Main Line to Darlington and Berwick. Bill Fawcett.*

The same Managing Committee was in action as on the N&C, and by September 1834 they were ready to advertise the contract for the tunnel[16] but complications had already arisen. In August the N&C gave notice of their intention to exercise their option of forming the line from Blaydon to Redheugh, while Robert William Brandling, brother of the BGH chairman John Brandling, announced his plan to form a line from Gateshead to South Shields and Monkwearmouth, a project which began as a means of exploiting his coal leases but rapidly blossomed into an ambitious rival.

Matters were quickly resolved with the N&C, on the basis that they would build the line from Blaydon as far as Derwenthaugh and the BGH would proceed east from there, reserving to the N&C the option of forming an additional line as far any Tyne crossing. This came nearer fruition with the N&C Act of 1835 which gave them powers to construct a low level bridge from Redheugh, at a height of about 20 feet above high water, and continue their line to a terminus at the Spital, approximately 80 feet higher. The existing powers for a route via a bridge at Scotswood were also retained, as an insurance.

It is significant that this Redheugh bridge was already conceived as a dual-purpose one, the directors having decided in October 1834[17] that it should be constructed 'if the Managing Committee shall think it expedient, so as to have two roadways: one for the carriages of the said company (N&C) and another for others' carriages, waggons horses, cattle etc as well as foot passengers' - the tolls on this traffic could be a valuable source of revenue. Other aspects of the scheme were less promising: the climb from the river bank to the Spital, partly in tunnel, would have entailed an incline worked by a stationary engine - though one has to remember that passenger trains at both Euston and Glasgow's Queen Street Station were worked this way originally.

Robert Brandling remained determined to build his own line from Gateshead, rather than link up with the BGH further east, and persuaded brother John to join him in May 1835 in publishing a prospectus for 'Brandling's Junction Railway' with a route approved by George Stephenson and Nicholas Wood (one of the BGH Managing Committee). John and Robert were lessees of the coalmining rights throughout an extensive area south of the Tyne, stretching almost from Gateshead to the coast, and their leases gave them the right to lay railways over the greater part of this land. Robert obtained an Act for his railway on 30 July 1835, and on 7 September the Brandling Junction Railway Company was formed, with a capital of £110,000. This bought out the Brandlings' personal investment, rights and wayleaves and obtained a further Act of Parliament on 7 June 1836[18].

This left no future for the BGH and at a shareholders meeting in February 1836 the directors were authorised to proceed with the sale of the railway and its parliamentary powers to the N&C. The company had only completed about a mile of line, and it was left to the N&C to finish the route from Blaydon to Askew's Quay, below Redheugh, where the first passenger station to serve Gateshead was formally opened on 1 March 1837. Passengers and goods for Newcastle were conveyed across the Tyne by boat to a station at No. 66, The Close, formerly a riverside mansion.

The Brandling Junction Railway took over construction of the Redheugh Incline at an improved gradient of 1 in 23, though this still entailed haulage by a stationary engine at the summit. This opened on 15 January 1839, together with a line carried across Gateshead largely on a low viaduct, instead of the BGH tunnel, to a station at Oakwellgate, from which a self-acting (gravity-operated) incline led down to a riverside quay at the east end of Hillgate. Thus the N&C obtained access to a shipping place below the Tyne Bridge, but hardly by the most convenient of routes. The Brandling Junction main line from Oakwellgate to South Shields and Monkwearmouth opened to mineral traffic on 29 August and passengers on 5 September 1839. A route had been achieved which was much more useful than that of the BGH, in that it extended to the river mouth and to the Wear.

Though hard to credit in its present devastated condition, Oakwellgate had been an attractive street with a number of large Georgian houses, but men of means were moving their homes out of the town centre and the railway helped to accelerate the change. The Brandling depot was built on open land just behind the existing buildings on the east side of the street, a carriage ramp being all that separated them from the approximately 20 feet high mound created to form a yard at the level of the railway viaduct. This bore offices and sheds but no buildings of any architectural pretension, since Robert Brandling already had his eyes fixed on an extension into Newcastle. This was wise, since the passenger traffic was transferred on 1 September 1844 to a new station at Greene's Field, but Oakwellgate remained a goods and coal depot, and its sturdy retaining walls are still evident today.

Hoping to cross the Tyne
While the Newcastle & Carlisle Railway was struggling to complete its route, trunk railways were beginning to make their way up from London. It may seem strange that Tyneside's business community had little interest in projecting a main line to the south, in view of the rapid growth in the coal and engineering industries. Their freight transport needs were adequately met, however, by coastal shipping, especially with the introduction of larger and faster steamships and the improvements which iron was bringing to the shipbuilding industry. For them the principal role of railways was still to provide access to the coast and rivers.

By contrast, down in Darlington the predominantly Quaker business community had already warmed to the future potential of trunk railways and were keen to place their town on the main line from London. They therefore promoted a Great North of England Railway (GNER) as an extension of the main line from Yorkshire through Darlington to the Tyne. It obtained a first Act on 4 July 1836 for a line from Newcastle to Darlington, and a second on 30 June 1837 for the section from Darlington to York, together with a branch to the City of Durham - the main line being intended to avoid the city and pass through Shincliffe. The engineer was Thomas Storey, a relative of George Stephenson and one of his two resident engineers on the construction of the Stockton & Darlington Railway[19]. Like the present main line, Storey's route approached Gateshead along the Team Valley but continued directly towards a river crossing close to the site of the present Redheugh Bridge.

The promotion of the GNER created a problem for the Newcastle & Carlisle Railway. The N&C wished to hold the key to Newcastle, and the original understanding was that the GNER would come down to the riverside and form a junction with the N&C at the south end of their proposed Tyne bridge. Storey then reconsidered his company's needs, recognising that the Spital incline was not a desirable feature and that the GNER could easily approach the Tyne at a much higher level. At a meeting on 18 August 1836[20] the N&C offered the GNER a route 'at any higher level if required', the works to remain the property of the N&C but the GNER paying a share of the cost and a toll. John Clayton was present at the meeting and foresaw no difficulty in obtaining extra land for a GNER passenger and goods depot adjacent to that proposed by the N&C.

This implies a readiness on the part of the N&C to consider a bridge on two levels, Storey having informed his directors after the meeting that their crossing would have to be about 74 feet above the river; he also anticipated later developments by suggesting a better crossing point downstream but this would have entailed a change of route well outside the Parliamentary limits of deviation and so was shelved. There was also a party among the N&C directors which favoured abandoning the low-level crossing and incline and altering their own route to cross the Tyne as a locomotive line at a high level[21].

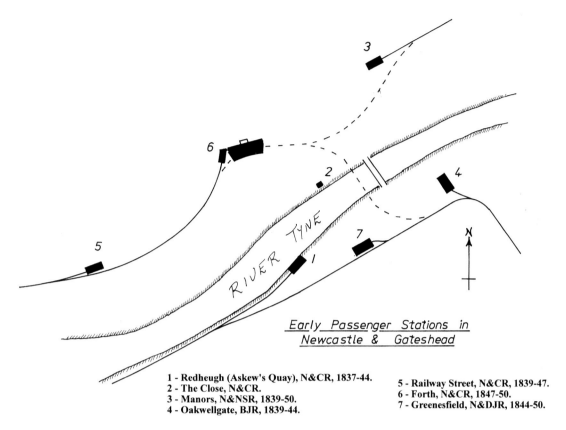

1 - Redheugh (Askew's Quay), N&CR, 1837-44.
2 - The Close, N&CR.
3 - Manors, N&NSR, 1839-50.
4 - Oakwellgate, BJR, 1839-44.

5 - Railway Street, N&CR, 1839-47.
6 - Forth, N&CR, 1847-50.
7 - Greenesfield, N&DJR, 1844-50.

Fig. 1.5 Early Passenger Stations in Newcastle and Gateshead. Bill Fawcett.

Further complications came with the Brandling Junction, which wished to share any high-level crossing into Newcastle and also hoped to become the outlet for a larger hinterland through a connection with the Durham Junction Railway. Meanwhile Richard Grainger had become involved, publishing *'A proposal for concentrating the termini of the Newcastle & Carlisle, the Great North of England and proposed Edinburgh Railways'*. Grainger pointed out the difficulties involved in connecting the proposed depot at the Spital with any line to Edinburgh as well as to the Newcastle & North Shields Railway, which had recently obtained an Act for a line commencing on the east side of Pilgrim Street in Newcastle, and whose deputy chairman was John Hodgson Hinde of Elswick Hall.

Grainger's solution was to move the river crossing upstream to Elswick and build extensive depots on a site further away from the city centre but with plenty of space for expansion. He proposed using the existing N&C powers to form a goods line from Elswick to the Tyne Bridge and, indeed, urged adoption of the original plan to extend this through the bridge to the Quayside. He also offered to build a new road, 60 feet wide, from the depots to the centre of Newcastle. This was just part of a grand plan. Though Elswick Hall remained among its gardens[22], industry was spreading along the riverside while Grainger hoped to develop a residential suburb on the Elswick Estate; he already owned the land proposed for the railway depots, and in January 1839 agreed to purchase the entire estate from John Hodgson Hinde.

Grainger's idea was taken up by the GNER, which sent a deputation to him early in October 1836, while also requesting Storey to prepare estimates for a high-level bridge, hoping to persuade the N&C to give up their scheme and use a GNER bridge instead. Grainger's response is set out in a letter of 12 October[23], in which he agreed to sell up to 8 acres of land for the depots at a price well below its commercial value, to erect within 12 months a bridge to serve both railways - which he optimistically estimated could be built for under £25,000, and to ensure that the necessary road access was ready.

Grainger claimed that the N&C were ready to form the branch from the Elswick depot to the Tyne Bridge, but this was perhaps a misreading of one of Clayton's numerous attempts to negotiate between the parties. The N&C remained committed to having their own bridge at Redheugh, and discussions continued through November to see if one could be provided which reconciled the needs of all three railways. The problems posed by their differences in level were highlighted in a discussion in the Newcastle Town Council on 9 November 1836, at which a crucial resolution was passed urging that the Tyne be bridged at a height which would secure a locomotive route for all three companies into the centre of the town. For the N&C, however, a high-level bridge implied major ancillary works, with an embankment beginning the climb to the bridge somewhere in the vicinity of Dunston. With the line to Carlisle still far from complete, the company could not afford this and the talks broke down.

The GNER continued discussions with the Brandling Junction and Durham Junction, though it proved wary of their attempt to persuade it to abandon parts of its own route in favour of using their lines[24]. The GNER remained committed to its own route and high-level bridge over the Tyne but financial problems were to determine otherwise. The company had intended to begin building the line across County Durham before starting on the much easier section down the Vale of York, but a year after obtaining the first Act little had been achieved and the tenders for works had proved to be much more costly than expected. In August 1837, therefore, having recently got their Act for the line from York to Darlington, they decided to start with this. The first contracts were let in October but the work cost more than twice Storey's original estimate and was not completed until January 1841. Even then the condition of the works precluded the running of a passenger service and the formal opening was delayed until 30 March, with public traffic beginning the following day. Though it soon built up a healthy traffic, the GNER was in no state to consider proceeding with the line from Darlington to Newcastle, and so coach services linking existing lines were used to fill the gap[25].

Reaching Newcastle
By the beginning of 1837 the Newcastle & Carlisle directors, though determined to have an independent route into Newcastle and unwilling to delay any longer, were losing faith in their low-level Redheugh bridge scheme. In February they asked Blackmore to prepare plans and estimates for this and a number of alternatives, including a crossing at Scotswood and high-level bridges at 80 feet and 100 feet above Askew's Quay, which could have accommodated the other railways. Their choice fell on the 1829 Parliamentary line, with its bridge at Scotswood, providing a route which could be worked throughout by locomotives. Adopting the Thornton Street Branch instead of the riverside approach gave access towards the town centre under the company's existing powers, although the final steep section of that route was to be replaced by a line to a terminus south of the Infirmary, for which a new Act was required.

After so much uncertainty the line from Blaydon into Newcastle was at last formally opened by the directors on 21 May 1839 but even this was a largely ceremonial occasion and the railway did not open to passengers until 21 October, although it was almost immediately closed by landslips, caused by heavy rain. The new line crossed the Tyne by a low, timber-trussed bridge and finished at a temporary station, half a mile from the town centre, in Railway Street. To serve the river, the company began building a new quay upstream of the Skinner Burn with access by an incline, to be worked by a stationary engine. Constructed by Grainger, the quay was virtually complete by June 1841[26] but, belatedly realising its doubtful value, the company never completed the incline and its site was eventually absorbed into the Elswick gasworks.

Meanwhile rails had also been snaking along the north bank of the Tyne east of Newcastle. Early schemes for a railway to North Shields, projected in 1830 and 1831, envisaged a line commencing on the riverside at Newcastle, where a junction could be made with the 1829 Parliamentary route of the Newcastle & Carlisle. When an Act was finally passed, on 21 June 1836, it was for a railway 7 miles long and commencing on the east side of Pilgrim Street, a short distance north of the Royal Arcade, from which there was no prospect of forming any link with the N&C. The engineer of the Newcastle & North Shields Railway (N&NS) was Robert Nicholson (1808-1858) but the most dramatic contribution to the works of the line was made by John and Benjamin Green, who designed its most significant engineering features, the viaducts across the Ouseburn Valley, between Newcastle and Byker, and Willington Dene, between Wallsend and Howdon (Plate 1.2). These carried two tracks on laminated timber arches, constructed on the Wiebeking system and supported by tall stone piers.

Plate 1.2   The Ouseburn Viaduct of the Newcastle & North Shields Railway, depicted by John Wilson Carmichael. Bill Fawcett collection.

John Green (1787-1852) was an architect and civil engineer, practising in Newcastle. In 1829 he was appointed architect to the Duke of Northumberland's local estates, designing farm buildings throughout Northumberland[27] and by 1837 had taken into partnership his son Benjamin (1813-1858), who seems to have been responsible for their more flamboyant architectural designs, including the stations later built for the Newcastle & Berwick Railway. John Green had supervised the construction of Scotswood Suspension Bridge and drew on this experience to submit two designs for a road bridge over the Tees at Blackwell, just outside Darlington[28], one being a suspension bridge but the other a timber structure which may well have anticipated the railway viaducts, since he had already experimented with laminated timber arches as early as 1827[29]. The appearance of the viaducts is well known since they were reported in a paper read by Benjamin Green to the Institution of Civil Engineers[30], earning him their Telford Medal, and, though the timberwork was later reconstructed in iron to the designs of Thomas Elliot Harrison and the Ouseburn bridge was subsequently widened, great care was taken to replicate the original form. The Greens also used their laminated arches for a tied-arch bridge over the Shields road at Walker, and later for the Wear bridge of the West Durham Railway at Willington.

Unlike some other promoters, the North Shields directors got on briskly with the work: the viaducts were advertised to contractors in August 1836[31], and the line opened on 22 June 1839. At the North Shields station the Greens covered the tracks and platforms with a roof carried by laminated timber arches borne on cast-iron columns (Fig. 5.4). This seems to be the earliest instance of curved ribs being used to support a trainshed roof in Britain, and they presumably envisaged a more ambitious version for the terminus in Newcastle. The Pilgrim Street station was, however, postponed on account of uncertainty over links to other lines and the possibility of forming a joint station.

The North Shields railway entered Newcastle by an embankment across Pandon Dene after which an impressive stone bridge, designed by the Greens, was provided to carry it over an intended extension of Trafalgar Street. The line continued at a raised level, between stone retaining walls, past the new prison and towards Pilgrim Street but then ended abruptly at what would have been the eastern boundary of the station premises. As a temporary measure, two platforms were provided on top of this formation with an open-fronted waiting shed alongside the departure platform (Plate 1.3). A coal depot was built on the south side and the station acquired a gate office in characteristic Benjamin Green style, which lasted into the nineteen-sixties. Early on this terminus became popularly known as the station 'in the Manors' and when the name 'Manors' was transferred to a new station, opened in 1850, the old depot began to take its name from Carliol Square instead.

Plate 1.3   The Newcastle terminus of the North Shields Railway at Manors. Taken long after its closure to passengers, this view looks west towards Pilgrim Street; the bridge over Trafalgar Street - which still exists - is somewhere behind the photographer. The waiting shed on the right shows the temporary nature of the original station, but the railway's substructure and a small Gothic gate office survived into the nineteen-sixties, only to be demolished for the motorway. Newcastle City Libraries.

Joining Newcastle and Darlington

The Great North of England Railway's failure to proceed north of Darlington was no doubt a disappointment to many but for one man it offered a golden opportunity. In 1841 George Hudson was chairman of the York & North Midland Railway, a necessary link in the main line from London but a very modest one - not quite 24 miles long. Three years later he had completed the link between Darlington and Gateshead and was chairman of the mighty Midland Railway, thereby giving him control of the main line as far south as Leicester. By 1848 his writ ran from Bristol to Berwick and he had fully earned *Punch's* satiric title of 'Railway King'.

In 1841 there was strong rivalry between the protagonists of rival routes from London to Scotland passing up the east and west sides of England. George and Robert Stephenson were determined to push forward the East Coast Route, so Robert revived a scheme first proposed to the GNER in November 1837 by his close friend T. E. Harrison, engineer of the Durham Junction Railway. This minimised the amount of new construction by making use of existing railways for about 40% of the distance. A new line was required from Darlington to Rainton Meadows, much of it over the GNER Parliamentary route, after which traffic would use the Durham Junction, Stanhope & Tyne and Brandling Junction railways. The GNER was ready to transfer powers in respect of its Parliamentary route north of Darlington to a new company and, though the share market was in one of its troughs at this time, Hudson persuaded the companies involved throughout the route from Leicester to Gateshead, even including the Newcastle & Carlisle, to guarantee the scheme for ten years and take up shares, thus getting it off the ground[32].

The Newcastle & Darlington Junction Railway (N&DJ) got its Act on 18 June 1842 and, with typical Hudson briskness, the railway was completed in two years. Credit is due also to Robert Stephenson as Engineer-in-Chief and T. E. Harrison as resident engineer. A small portion of the line, including the branch to Durham (which was bypassed on its east side), opened on 15 April 1844 and the public opening of the entire route took place on the anniversary of the Battle of Waterloo, 18 June. A special train left Euston station at 5.03 in the morning and arrived at an elegant new terminus in Greene's Field, Gateshead, at 2.24 p.m., having travelled 303 miles. By then Hudson had secured the consent of the parties involved to cancel the original lease agreement of 1841 so placing the company firmly under his control.

Hudson Consolidating a Bridgehead

While the Newcastle and Darlington Junction Railway had been getting underway, the affairs of the Brandling Junction were drifting into chaos. The construction costs had been excessive and the management left a lot to be desired. In 1843 a shareholders' Committee of Investigation revealed that dividends had been paid out of capital rather than revenue, something at which Hudson was also adept but which he managed to conceal until 1849. A reorganisation put the Brandling on to a sound footing but, with the opening of the N&DJ, Hudson decided to embark on a takeover campaign. When the Brandling failed to accept his terms he proposed the construction of a new line from Washington to Gateshead in direct competition and this had the desired effect, an agreement being signed on 13 August 1844 under which he purchased the line with possession from 1 September; he then transferred it to the N&DJ. By October 1845 the entire route from York to the Tyne was under Hudson's control, his major coup having been to buy out the Great North of England Railway, offering terms so favourable they could not refuse. At the same time, negotiations were underway regarding the extension of the main line north from the Tyne though Hudson's strategy for this, assuming he had one, is very hard to discern.

In 1839, with their timber-arched railway viaducts very much in the public eye, the Greens had proposed a high level road bridge across the Tyne built on the same principles, but with the longest spans extended from a maximum of 128 feet at Willington Dean to 280 feet (Plate 1.4). A prospectus for a company to build the bridge[33] was issued in November and, though nothing came of this, the scheme was revived two years later on a slightly altered alignment heading just to the west of the castle of Newcastle. At a meeting in October 1841 Benjamin Green explained how the bridge could be adapted for railway use, and he also devised a route linking up with the Newcastle & North Shields Railway, thereby anticipating the alignment eventually adopted. A company was formed to promote the scheme but the financial climate which proved so discouraging to the GNER was no kinder to bridge promoters.

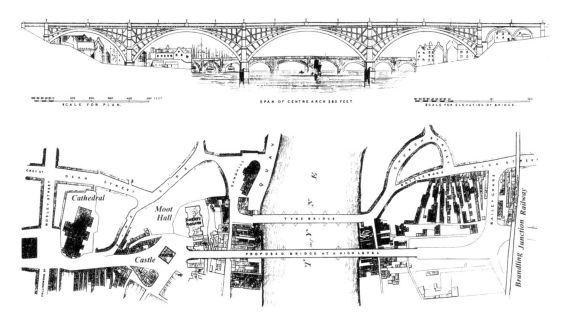

Plate 1.4 John & Benjamin Green's 1839 design for a high-level road bridge across the Tyne, with Mylne's bridge in the background. Tyne & Wear Archives.

As the stock market improved and the main line progressed towards the Tyne there was a revival of activity and in 1843 the Parliamentary deadline of 30 November saw plans deposited for 3 rival schemes: the Greens', one by John Dobson and another by Richard Grainger. This time, however, there were serious backers on hand. Newcastle Town Council appointed a committee to consider them and on 20 December met to decide which should receive their endorsement[34]. Grainger's scheme was easily disposed of. He proposed a high level road bridge based, like Stevenson's 1828 proposal, on the piers of Mylne's existing bridge only this time not just the upper arches but their supporting columns were to be of iron. Though this would have lightened the load, compared with Stevenson's masonry piers, the committee had serious doubts as to whether Mylne's structure could cope.

Dobson's proposal was an intriguing one, apparently a final effort by the Newcastle & Carlisle Railway to make themselves the key to any railway crossing of the Tyne as part of a rather unrealistic ambition to become the springboard for a 'Central' route into Scotland, from a junction near Gilsland on the Cumberland boundary. He proposed a high-level crossing of the Tyne with four river spans of 141 feet each and an arch over the Close on an alignment well upstream of the present High Level Bridge and heading towards a station on the site of the western half of the present Central Station. To the N&C he offered three alternatives[35]:

i. A railway and footway on one level, the deck being 40 feet wide, and the estimated cost being £78,000

ii. A double-decker bridge with a railway on top and road underneath, at an estimated cost of £108,000

iii.A single deck bridge, 60 feet wide, with a road and railway alongside, at an estimated cost of £98,000.

Unfortunately the company's records give no hint of its mode of construction although the town council's minutes indicate the use of iron.

The Greens' scheme came to the council with the advantage of a backer with financial muscle. In September Hudson had offered a guaranteed return of 3% to the promoters, with the bridge being used for railway purposes, though not closing his mind to the possibility of exploiting the N&C scheme instead, as a letter from George Stephenson, dated 1 November, reveals[36, 37]. In this he urged Hudson not to give up the Tyne crossing 'to these people who have no interest in the Eastern Route' (i.e. the East Coast route to Scotland), arguing 'have we not a right to carry the line through Newcastle in such a manner as will most effectually promote the property invested in the Eastern lines of England. No bridge across the Tyne can be made without your assistance! You have the power in your hands, sometimes with the assistance of your friends.'

Hudson and Stephenson duly joined the committee of promoters of the Greens' bridge and Robert Stephenson came on board as joint consulting engineer, yet when the proposal came before the council it proved to be a road bridge only. Impressed by Hudson's ability to see the scheme through, and considering the Dobson bridge to be too far upriver for road users, the council gave him their backing. At the same time Hudson's Newcastle & Darlington Junction Railway was preparing a Parliamentary Bill to extend its powers to cover the construction of the Greenesfield station and its approaches. The Act, obtained on 22 May 1844 when that station was nearly completed, also included powers to make the road bridge across the Tyne and its approaches extending from Greenesfield to St. Nicholas' Square in Newcastle, with a stipulation that there should be no more than four river piers as well as requirements as to minimum height[38].

Hudson had thus acquired both the Greens' scheme and parliamentary powers to carry it out, yet no progress had been made towards carrying the East Coast Main Line north of the Tyne. The Stephensons were determined to pursue a route through coastal Northumberland to Berwick, to meet the North British Railway, which received its Act on 4 July 1844 for a line from Edinburgh to Berwick. It is clear from George Stephenson's letter, already quoted, that he had envisaged a line passing through Newcastle and linking up with the North Shields Railway as a stepping stone to the North. However, the adoption of the road bridge scheme suggests that the railway crossing was now to be made further down the Tyne. In September 1836, during the discussions about a Redheugh crossing, T. E. Harrison had pointed out the possibility of bridging the Tyne economically at Bill Quay, just over two miles below the Tyne Bridge[39]. The river narrows again here and a convenient link could readily have been made between the main line from the south and the route soon to be adopted to Berwick, leaving Greenesfield as the principal station for both Gateshead and Newcastle.

Though this seems to have been Hudson's unpublicised intention during the early months of 1844, it had a number of drawbacks. The issue of wounded pride in Newcastle was not the most serious of these, but might weaken support for his advance on Berwick, while it was clear that Greenesfield would not be allowed to function as a truly 'Central' station for both towns. Some North Shields traffic would continue running to Manors, while the Newcastle & Carlisle was finalising plans to build its own terminus near the Infirmary, indeed Thomas Oliver jumped the gun in his 1844 map of Newcastle by showing a station there which never existed[40]. Thus there would be interchange problems and extra cartage costs arising from multiple termini. In addition, while a Bill Quay crossing would save the cost of forming a railway from the Castle to Manors as part of a Newcastle crossing, this had to be weighed against the cost of building two high-level bridges over the Tyne.

In February 1844 Hudson secured his shareholders' consent to prepare surveys for the extension to Berwick, while in August they agreed to the promotion of a Newcastle & Berwick Railway Company, to be leased in perpetuity by the N&DJ at a rent sufficient to guarantee a return of 5%. Hudson now needed friends: interest in railway investment was warming up into the blaze which became known as the 'Railway Mania' and a significant rival had appeared - Brunel's atmospheric Northumberland Railway. So the Tyne railway crossing was fixed between Gateshead and Newcastle on the Greens' alignment even though as late as November 1844 it seems that Hudson was intent on still using Greenesfield and had no wish to build a major new passenger station in Newcastle.

The Newcastle & Carlisle Railway, as the price of their parliamentary support for the Newcastle & Berwick scheme, insisted on Hudson's participation in a joint station in Newcastle. They had already been offered this by the Northumberland Railway, not surprisingly. At a meeting in January 1845, attended also by George Stephenson,[41] Hudson finally confirmed his readiness to participate in a joint station partly on that site at the Spital which had been the subject of so much fruitless discussion during the previous decade.

Epilogue

Without trespassing on the details which enliven later chapters of this story, it may be helpful to sum up the remainder of Hudson's career on Tyneside. 1845 was a year of success: the Newcastle & Berwick Railway got its Act, Parliament sanctioned the purchase of the Newcastle & North Shields Railway, and the works to the north got underway. In July 1846 Parliament approved the lease and eventual purchase of the GNER by the Newcastle & Darlington Junction, which changed its name to the more appropriate York & Newcastle Railway, merging with its northern partner in August 1847 to become the York, Newcastle & Berwick Railway (YNB).

So far things had been going well but the stock market was back on its downward cycle and Hudson was unable to continue manufacturing the large dividends which had for so long kept his shareholders content. A probing question at the February 1849 meeting of YNB shareholders drew out the information that Hudson had profited on the resale of GNER shares to his own company and, while this could have been a genuine mistake, the revelations of the committee of shareholders appointed to investigate the matter soon ousted the Railway King from this and other chairs. The disclosure that Hudson's dividends, the market leaders, had in no small way drawn on the shareholders' own capital caused a drastic slump in railway share prices generally. These recovered but by 1851 it seemed that the YNB was heading for a mutually destructive rivalry with the Leeds Northern Railway, which was extending to Stockton and had its sights set further north. Unusually, commonsense prevailed and in 1853 the two companies entered a working arrangement with Hudson's first railway, the York & North Midland, culminating in their amalgamation in August 1854 to form the North Eastern Railway.

Plate 2.1   The former trainshed of Greenesfield Station transformed into the Erecting Shop of Gateshead Works. View looking west, with the rear wall of the station, a fragment of which still remains, on the left. The structure carrying the overhead crane is independent of the roof structure. The locomotives under construction are 4-6-0s of the second batch of Wilson Worsdell's Class S, dating the photograph to 1906.   Ken Hoole collection.

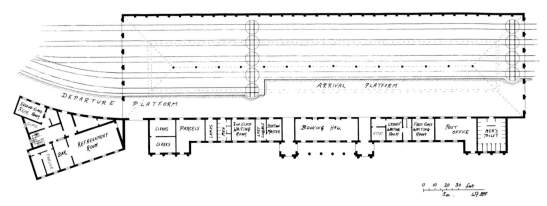

Fig. 2.1   Ground plan of Greenesfield Station in June 1844. The trains entered from the east (left) end.   Bill Fawcett.

Chapter 2

GATESHEAD GREENESFIELD STATION

BILL FAWCETT

The Greenesfield passenger station of the Newcastle & Darlington Junction Railway was the first to be erected in either Newcastle or Gateshead which had not been conceived as a more-or-less temporary expedient; it is therefore ironic that it should have lasted only six years in that role, before being converted into a locomotive workshop, having been bypassed by the High Level Bridge and superseded by Newcastle Central Station.

Writing to George Hudson in July 1843, John Hodgson Hinde, chairman of the promoters of the Greens' Tyne Bridge, urged the merits of the site at Greene's Field, close to both the proposed bridgehead and the Redheugh Incline: 'you should tell the Newcastle & Carlisle Railway you've fixed on a station at Greene's Field and will make them an offer of accommodation in it using the Brandling Junction incline to get traffic from the South to Carlisle'[1]. Hinde saw this as a way of pre-empting the N&C's Tyne Bridge scheme but, despite his endorsement of the Greens' bridge, Hudson was unwilling to fully commit himself. In September 1843 he and Robert Stephenson decided that the modest Oakwellgate terminus was unsuitable for their needs[2] but the plans for a station at Greene's Field were not sanctioned by the N&DJ Board until February 1844, only four months short of the planned opening date for the line. Not everyone was pleased at the thought of Tyneside's principal station being located in Gateshead, and the *Newcastle Journal* sourly commented that it would 'be so constructed that its materials may hereafter be removed to the north side of the Tyne'[3].

On 14 February 1844 the main contract was let to Charles John Pearson, a leading Gateshead builder, who pledged himself to a completion date of 14 May - a prodigious achievement even by Victorian standards. Frost and snow delayed a start on site but meanwhile the ironfounders Hawks Crawshay, then Gateshead's largest employer, got on with casting the trainshed columns and fabricating its wrought-iron roof trusses. The first of these was raised into position on 27 April to an accompaniment of cheers and waving flags while a fortnight later, with the shed almost complete, the local Mechanics' Institution sought permission to hold a fundraising soiree within. This was denied because of the need to get on with laying the platform and tracks, but extensive celebrations took place at the opening on 18 June[4].

Greenesfield Station (Fig. 2.1) represented the latest technology in station design. It was a terminus - even the Carlisle trains, coming up the Redheugh Incline from the west, reversed into the station - and at terminal stations Robert Stephenson normally employed separate arrival and departure platforms on opposite sides of the tracks, as the North Shields Railway had done at Manors. Greenesfield, however, had tracks running through to sidings at the west end and so, to avoid passengers crossing the lines, a single platform was provided but stepped back to provide separate bays for arrivals and departures.

The track and platform layout having been determined by the engineers, the station was designed by George Townsend Andrews, a York architect who was a close friend of George Hudson and had extensive experience of designing railway buildings, including the first York Station. At York Andrews had adopted the form of wrought-iron truss popularised by Robert Stephenson and Charles Fox[5] through their use of it at Euston. However, they had used a fireproof construction, fixing slates onto iron purlins using copper fastenings. Quite apart from any practical drawbacks such as condensation and a tendency for the slates to lift in high winds, this will have given a dark internal appearance to an otherwise attractive structure. So Andrews used lightweight purlins carrying wooden planking laid diagonally, which contributed to the rigidity of the structure, cladding this with slates[6]. The Greenesfield roof was in two spans, the valley borne on an elegant cast-iron arcade, and, characteristically, he returned the spans across each end to create a hip which helped to integrate the trainshed visually with the office building in front. To support the half-trusses of the hip he carried the trainshed wall across each end, providing flat-lintelled openings (presumably with concealed cast-iron beams) for the tracks. The roof was ventilated along the two ridges by a raised glass skylight with louvred sides.

An extensive range of offices was provided in a tall, single-storey building facing north across the Tyne. In the centre was a spacious booking hall fronted by an Ionic portico (Fig. 2.2); at the ends were pavilions with direct access from the street into the parcels office and the room

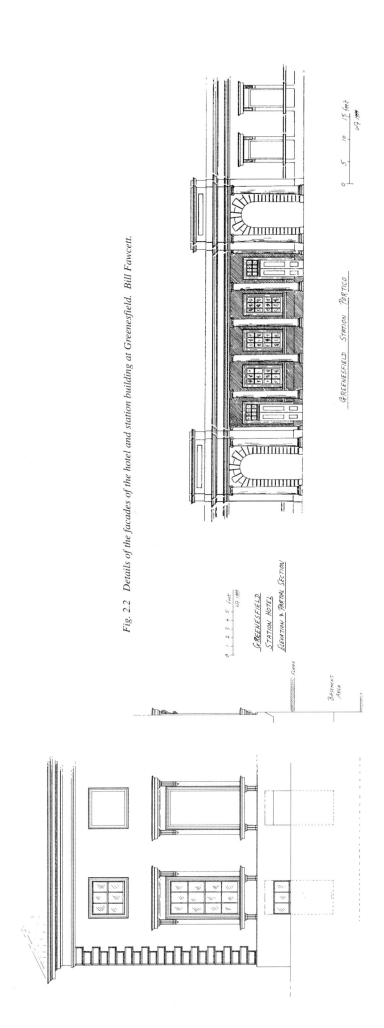

Fig. 2.2   Details of the facades of the hotel and station building at Greenesfield.   Bill Fawcett.

GREENESFIELD STATION PORTICO

0   5   10   15 feet

GREENESFIELD
STATION HOTEL
ELEVATION & PARTIAL SECTION

0 1 2 3 4 5 feet

FLOORS

BASEMENT
AREA

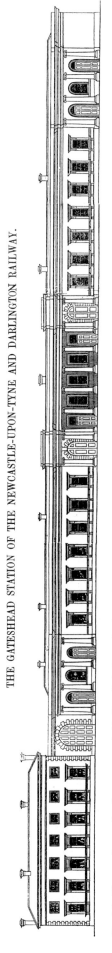

THE GATESHEAD STATION OF THE NEWCASTLE-UPON-TYNE AND DARLINGTON RAILWAY.

Fig. 2.3   The complete station frontage, recorded in Douglas's 'Records of Remarkable Events connected with the Borough of Gateshead', 1844.   Gateshead Central Library.

allocated to the post office, since the mails were now travelling by train. The hierarchy of passengers was carefully observed, with separate waiting rooms for first and second class passengers - none at all for the numerous third class - and a ladies' waiting room, with its own attendant[7]. Refreshment rooms were provided in a block at the east end of the station, with access only from the platform and having a small number of bedrooms above granting it the title of hotel, while the kitchens were in a raised basement below. The first-class refreshment room was the main feature, with pairs of pilasters flanking the bar at one end and the sideboard recess at the other. Externally, the hotel was conceived as a modestly lavish Italian palazzo, scrupulously detailed and a visual foil to the long facade of the station offices, whose Ionic order was continued in the shallow pilasters punctuating the trainshed openings.

At its opening, Greenesfield Station seemed to symbolise Gateshead's new civic pride. Its approaches from West Street and the proposed high-level road bridge were viewed as a civic space providing an opportunity to create, on a small scale, something of the urban elegance achieved by Grainger in Newcastle - with Pearson, a prominent local figure, perhaps playing the role of Grainger. Even the town hall moved from Oakwellgate into a house nearby.

In just eighteen months these hopes were doomed. Hudson committed himself to a new station in Newcastle, and the route to the High Level Bridge left Greenesfield out on a limb. When Central Station opened in August 1850, Greenesfield closed, replaced by a modest stone box designed by Dobson and clinging to the approach viaduct. Little time was lost in finding a new use. The York, Newcastle & Berwick Railway, as it had become, decided to concentrate its locomotive repairs at Gateshead and to convert the station into workshops. On 4 October 1851 the *Newcastle Journal* reported that the site for the necessary extensions had been staked out and Hawks Crawshay had again got the contract for the iron roofing, while Robert Stephenson & Co. would be supplying the machine tools.

Greenesfield Station came through its initial reconstruction surprisingly well. The trainshed was barely altered and the extension comprised another two roof spans of similar design built on to the front of the station offices, which entailed the removal of the portico and the projecting fronts of the end pavilions[8]. The hotel was converted into offices, with Edward Fletcher - the YNB Locomotive Superintendent - housed in the former refreshment room, and the exterior of the extension was designed to harmonise with it although adopting an appropriately more rugged style. With the formation of the North Eastern Railway in 1854, Fletcher took charge of all its engines and Gateshead became the headquarters of his department and the company's principal locomotive works. Within a decade the works had expanded across the plateau to the west, culminating in a very large engine shed housing 5 turntables and capable of stabling 76 locomotives[9]. The site left little room for further enlargement yet for half a century, despite the development of the former Stockton & Darlington Railway workshops at Darlington, Gateshead produced most of the larger locomotives of the NER. Eventually, however, the constraints proved too much; major extensions were made at Darlington and the construction of new locomotives at Gateshead ceased in 1910, with the Chief Mechanical Engineer and his design staff moving to Darlington on 1 October[10]. The works had become Gateshead's largest single employer and the consequences were drastic, with half the workforce moving to Darlington and only 1,500 remaining in 1911 compared with over 3,300 two years earlier[11].

Gateshead Works continued to carry out repairs and still provided over a thousand jobs until 1932, when it was closed by the London & North Eastern Railway - an understandable economy by the hard-pressed company but a severe blow to the already-depressed town[12]. The Second World War brought about its re-opening, and the works survived until 1959. The original station building was demolished at Easter 1968 and many of the later workshops have since gone, but the former hotel and the 1851-2 workshop building remain, albeit precariously, and deserve to be given a new lease of life as the last reminder of an important phase in the town's history. To get an idea of what Greenesfield Station was like inside, a trip to Durham is strongly recommended, where the original station in Gilesgate survives, well-tended, as the outlet of a builders' merchant.

Plate 2.2   The former Greenesfield Station, viewed from the west on 23 April 1949, showing the Ionic pilasters flanking the original openings for the tracks, later bricked up. The two lines coming in from the left are near the alignment of the route from the head of the Redheugh Incline, which originally gave access to the Newcastle & Carlisle Railway.   J.M. Fleming

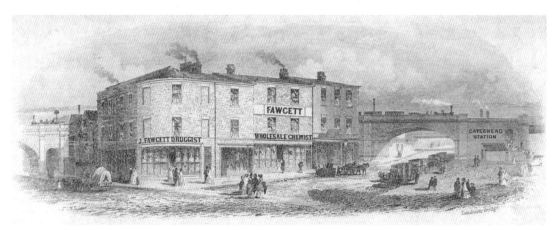

Plate 2.3   Vignette from the billhead of John Fawcett, chemist, showing the Brandling Junction's ornamental stone bridge over High Street on the left and the entrance to the replacement Gateshead station on the right.   Gateshead Central Library.

Plate 2.4   Gateshead West Station seen from the High Level Bridge approach. Designed by Thomas Prosser, it opened in 1868 to serve the Team Valley line and closed from 1 November 1965.   Gateshead Central Library.

Plate 2.5 A view over Gateshead Works about 1868. On the right can be seen the two-span roof of the original station with the 1852 extension beyond. To its left, in the centre of the picture, is the locomotive paint shop, formerly a two-road engine shed, dating from 1844 and designed by G.T. Andrews for the N&DJ. Adjoining it is the second Redheugh Incline winding house of 1844, with a water tank on top and tall chimney nearby. On the extreme left we glimpse a corner of the engine shed while in the background stretch the smiths' and boiler shops. (Newcastle City Libraries)

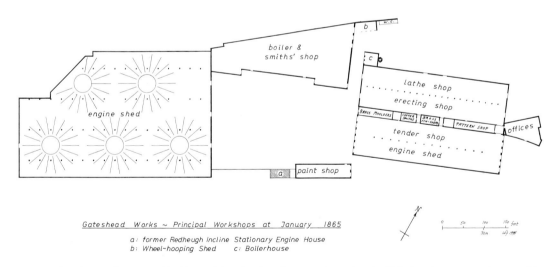

Gateshead Works ~ Principal Workshops at January 1865

a: former Redheugh Incline Stationary Engine House
b: Wheel~hooping Shed   c: Boilerhouse

Fig. 2.4 Plan showing the principal buildings of Gateshead Works as existing in January 1865, based on an NER plan signed by Edward Fletcher. A large stores block lay further east and is not shown. Bill Fawcett.

Chapter 3

BIOGRAPHICAL SKETCHES OF
JOHN DOBSON, THOMAS HARRISON,
GEORGE HUDSON AND ROBERT STEPHENSON

JOHN ADDYMAN & BILL FAWCETT

John Dobson

John Dobson was born in 1787 at Chirton, near North Shields, where his father was a prosperous market-gardener. At the age of 15 he became a pupil of David Stephenson (1757-1819), then Newcastle's leading architect and best known for his elliptical neo-classical church of All Saints which overlooks the city's quayside. In 1809, on completion of his pupillage, Dobson went to London and took lessons from the painter, John Varley[1].

On his return to Newcastle, Dobson built up a very extensive practice and became a prolific designer of churches and country villas. The most distinctive of these houses are Grecian in style but, as Howard Colvin has observed, 'agreeably free from the stereotyped pedantry of so many English Greek Revival houses of the same date'[2]. This can be judged in such ingenious Northumbrian villas as Nunnykirk and Longhirst. Dobson, however, was equally proud of his villas in Tudor dress, such as Holme Eden[3] and his particular favourite, Beaufront Castle, near Hexham, and adopted a similar style in his scheme for a terminus for the Newcastle & Carlisle Railway near the Forth[4]. So, despite a reputation as a classicist, Dobson was eclectic in his adoption and manipulation of styles, as evinced by the Baroque flavour of his original design for Central Station and his proposals for rebuilding the Newcastle Quayside following the disastrous Gateshead explosion of 1854, in which his architect son, Alexander, was tragically killed.

Dobson has long been identified with Richard Grainger's developments in Newcastle. Yet, while responsible for Eldon Square, the Royal Arcade and the Grainger Market interiors, he played little part in the rest of Grainger's prodigious output, though designing many other buildings in the city. These include the castellated, radial-plan prison which once dominated Carliol Square, near to the first Manors Station, and whose flavour can still be judged from the Sessions House at Morpeth, which looms up like an overblown medieval gatehouse.

In addition to his work for the Newcastle & Carlisle Railway, Dobson was a promoter of the first scheme to extend the East Coast Main Line north of the Tyne. In 1836 he was one of the authors of the prospectus for a 'Grand Eastern Union Railway' intended to continue from the Great North of England Railway through Berwick to Dunbar. The scheme was reported on favourably by George Stephenson, and for most of its length the route is close to that eventually adopted by the Newcastle & Berwick Railway[5].

Dobson clearly got on well with George Hudson. Having persuaded the Railway King to adopt his grandiose proposals for Central Station, he picked up further work in areas of Hudson's kingdom which survived the 1849 debacle. That year he replaced Hudson's former favourite G.T. Andrews as architect to the Whitby Building Company, designing some terraces reminiscent of Jesmond (a once-fashionable Newcastle suburb), and the huge and only half-completed Royal Crescent[6]. He also designed a large grain warehouse for Hudson at Sunderland Docks in 1856. Central Station was, however, the climax of Dobson's career, and while its portico was belatedly under construction he suffered a stroke, dying two years later on 8 January 1865.

Thomas Elliot Harrison

Thomas Elliot Harrison was born in Fulham, near London, on 4 April 1808 but is a true son of the North-East, having been educated at Houghton-le-Spring Grammar School following his father's move to Sunderland to start a shipbuilding yard. After a pupillage with William Chapman, Harrison went to London in 1829 to seek employment as a civil engineer. Rebuffed by Thomas Telford, who suggested - with singularly little foresight of the railway revolution - that there were few opportunities to achieve eminence in the profession, he filled in a year by working in the office of an accountant friend of his father. This experience proved invaluable in his subsequent career as a consulting engineer and railway administrator[7].

In 1830 Harrison met Robert Stephenson, who was to become a close friend and who employed him for two years on the preparation of parliamentary plans for the London & Birmingham Railway. Meanwhile his father, William Harrison, had become involved in the promotion of the 38 mile long 'Stanhope & Tyne Railroad', intended to open up the mineral resources of upper Weardale and the West Durham coalfield. With his father and uncle among the main promoters and Robert Stephenson appointed consulting engineer, it is not surprising that young Thomas was appointed resident engineer to supervise construction of the line - an invaluable professional experience. Before its completion in 1834, he was already engaged on the Durham Junction Railway, a satellite scheme. This entailed a high-level crossing of the River Wear near Penshaw, for which the architect John Green had already designed a cast-iron bridge. However, as it was Harrison's first major structure, he asked the advice of James Walker, then president of the Institution of Civil Engineers. Walker suggested a masonry design, based on Trajan's bridge at Alcantara. Completed in 1838, its river span of 160 feet is still the second-largest masonry arch on a British railway, and carried the East Coast Main Line from 1844 to 1872[8].

From 1841 until 1849 Harrison was associated with Stephenson throughout the construction of the main line from Darlington to Berwick, taking day-to-day charge of the entire work during the Engineer-in-Chief's necessarily long absences attending to other projects. By 1849 Stephenson, very-much overworked, was keen to reduce his commitments and Harrison was appointed Engineer to the York Newcastle & Berwick Railway, handling both the administration of their engineering department and the tasks normally associated with a consulting engineer. In 1850 he also became its General Manager and subsequently, convinced of the need for companies to co-operate rather than engage in mutually-destructive competition, led the negotiations which resulted in the formation of the North Eastern Railway in 1854.

At Harrison's request the NER separated the posts of Engineer and General Manager, and from October 1854 until his death on 20 March 1888 he was the company's Engineer-in-Chief - responsible for all civil and mechanical engineering functions. It was agreed that the NER should enjoy half his time, the rest being devoted to consultancy, and it became his habit to spend five months of the year based in Westminster looking after this business, while his brother-in-law Robert Hodgson, who had supervised the High Level Bridge construction, deputised on the NER. Harrison was much in demand as an arbitrator and consultant - on schemes such as the Severn Railway Bridge. He was also an adviser on the plans for the present Forth Bridge but had already begun to wind up his consultancy in order to concentrate on the NER, and was hard at work in his office at Central Station the day before his death, only a fortnight short of his eightieth birthday.

George Hudson

George Hudson was born in the small village of Howsham, near York, on 10 March 1800. His family were farmers but George followed a well-trodden path into the city, where he took apprenticeship to a linen-draper, becoming a partner in the business shortly before his twenty-first birthday. This steady progress received a jolt in 1827 when a wealthy great-uncle died, leaving George as the principal beneficiary and enabling him to branch out from tradesman to financial entrepreneur and local politician.

Hudson's role as leader of the York Tories and three-times Lord Mayor need not bother us, though it does impinge on his chairmanship of the city's first railway, the York & North Midland. Unlike other directors, he did not have to manage his other business interests and so became one of the first full-time railway promoters, active in the day-to-day running of the company to an extent that soon reduced other Board members to agreeable impotence. The YNM was engineered by the Stephensons, who fired Hudson with their enthusiasm for expanding the railway network and welcomed his ability to organise the finance needed, indeed Hudson became a partner in George Stephenson's Clay Cross collieries. Others were impressed. John Clayton came away from the meeting that organised the guarantees for the line from Darlington to Gateshead reporting that they had gone to York 'with gloomy countenances' but by the time Hudson finished speaking 'the light seemed to have suddenly broken upon us. We saw that the thing would be achieved and achieved soon; and we returned to our homes comfortable and happy'[9].

Making shareholders happy and encouraging them to carry on investing was one of George's skills, aided by enlightened accountancy. In the early days of railways many companies paid dividends out of capital while lines were still under construction in order to keep up the flow of investment. Hudson took this further and milked the capital raised to expand his railways in order to boost dividends well above the levels justified by traffic. For most of the eighteen-forties the YNM paid a dividend of 10%; Hudson set this; his secretary invented accounts to match and this fiction was then audited by George's brother-in-law, Richard Nicholson[10]. In the buoyant capital markets of 1844-5, Hudson had no difficulty raising the money needed for such expensive ventures as the High Level Bridge and Central Station; indeed new share issues by his companies were eagerly sought after and attracted high premiums.

By 1847 Hudson was at his peak, chairman of the mighty Midland Railway; the less-exalted and financially precarious Eastern Counties, and his two 'home' companies, the YNM and YNB. The inevitable downturn in the national economy had, however, begun, and the resulting slump in the availability of investment capital spelled doom to George since dividends could no longer be maintained and the real accounts could not be forever concealed from the probing of disgruntled shareholders.

Hudson's loss of his railway chairmanships in 1849 might not have been the end of his career. He had achieved a lot in rapidly expanding the British railway network, not just through his own lines but by stoking up the 'Railway Mania', the investment boom of the eighteen-forties. He was still chairman of Sunderland Dock Company and MP for that town. However, he had profited unreasonably in several transactions with his own railways and had to settle their demands. This and unsound speculations drove him into debt, and on losing his parliamentary seat in 1859 he fled to France. More vindictively than constructively, the NER pursued its claims against Hudson for a decade but from the beginning of 1870 the law no longer permitted imprisonment for debt and he was able to return to Britain, where he was reunited with his wife, and friends enabled them to live in reasonable comfort until his death on 14 December 1871.

Robert Stephenson

Given the numerous books about the Stephensons, even though we lack a definitive modern biography, this is no more than a sketch to put the events on Tyneside into the context of Robert's life[11]. Robert Stephenson was born at Willington Quay, about two miles west of North Shields, on 16 October 1803 and groomed by his father to become his partner and successor as a railway engineer. Although the South Street Locomotive Works, in Newcastle, was established in Robert's name and he made significant contributions to the early development of the steam locomotive, it was as Engineer-in-Chief of the London & Birmingham Railway from 1833 that he really made his mark. Thereafter he was very much in demand and, in his late thirties, was the world's leading railway engineer at the time work began on the Newcastle & Darlington Junction Railway.

The Newcastle & Berwick Railway was undertaken simultaneously with the Chester & Holyhead, with its mighty Britannia Bridge over the Menai. By then Robert was feeling the strain of his tremendous workload and his responsibilities for public safety, brought sharply into focus by the Dee Bridge tragedy of 1847. He ran down his activities in Britain but continued to engineer railways abroad, notably in Canada and Egypt, which gave him the opportunity to combine business with his favourite relaxation - sailing his first steam yacht *Titania* to Alexandria in 1850. By then he had been Engineer-in-Chief for over 1,800 miles of railway construction in Britain and abroad. Decades of overwork had taken their toll, however, and Robert died on 12 October 1859, just days before his fifty-sixth birthday.

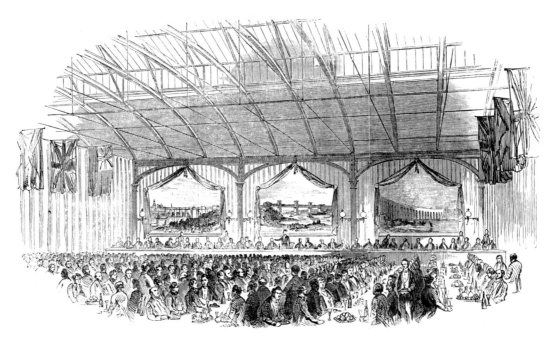

Plate 3.1 A dinner held in honour of Robert Stephenson in Newcastle Central Station 4 weeks before its opening in August 1850. Above the top table hang banners depicting the High Level Bridge, the Britannia Bridge over the Menai and the Royal Border Bridge across the Tweed. 'Illustrated London News' 10 August 1850.

The portrait of John Dobson is taken from a painting in the Laing Art Gallery; that of Thomas Elliot Harrison is reproduced by permission of the Institution of Civil Engineers, while George Hudson is depicted in John Leech's 'Punch' cartoon 'Off the Rail'.

Plate 4.1 A view of the river spans of the High Level Bridge looking east, taken before 1864 with the old Tyne Bridge in the background. The lamps on top of the piers of the H.L.B. have already disappeared - possibly as an economy they were never fitted. Newcastle City Libraries.

Plate 4.2 A composite picture of the bridges about the same date looking west. The tall chimney of Brown's corn mill is prominent at the Newcastle end of the main spans. Port of Tyne Authority/Les Paul collection.

Plate 4.3 View from the Quayside soon after the completion of the Swing Bridge in 1876 showing the original Team Valley Junction signal cabin placed centrally on its supporting girders at the end of the Gateshead approach. Ken Hoole collection.

Chapter 4

THE HIGH LEVEL BRIDGE

J. F. Addyman

Approval

At the end of 1844 George Hudson was extremely anxious to get support for the Stephensons' Newcastle and Berwick scheme and he asked Newcastle Town Council to hold a special meeting to decide their recommendations to Parliament. The meeting was held on 8th January 1845 and the brief report of a council sub-committee which had considered the rival schemes was printed in full in the minutes.[1] The sub-committee started by merely reporting on the alignments, gradients and levels which were quoted in the deposited plans for the Stephenson and Brunel schemes but commented favourably on Stephenson's plan to ". . . unite all the railway stations in one place near Neville Street". George Hudson, George Stephenson and T. E. Harrison ". . . attended for the purpose of giving any explanation or information that might be required, and to request the support of the Corporation to the Bill to be brought into Parliament in the ensuing session".

Hudson had just completed the substantial station at Gateshead Greenesfield from which the Brunel scheme proposed to start its "Gateshead Branch" in a westerly direction before crossing the Tyne at the site of the present Redheugh Bridge and terminating adjacent to Neville Street. To continue north the trains would have had to reverse and negotiate a 560ft. radius curve to pass under central Newcastle in a 2400yd. long tunnel[2]. The Stephenson scheme bypassed the new Gateshead station and Hudson's apparent willingness to provide another new station in Newcastle made the councillors suspicious, in spite of all that had passed before, that he did not want to bridge the Tyne leaving the terminus of the railway from the south in Gateshead and even starting the one to the north in Manors. Over half of the sub-committee's report focused on the bridge and outlined the guarantees and concessions that Hudson had been forced to give. "Mr. Hudson, at this interview, expressed his willingness to have a clause inserted in the bill, rendering it imperative on the Company to execute the bridge and the line through the town, as laid down on the plan, and depriving the Company of power to take toll on any part of the line between Newcastle and Berwick, unless the bridge over the Tyne, and the line through the town, were completed within the term of 5 years from the passing of the Act. . . . The question of the compatibility of a horse and carriage-way with a railway on the same bridge, was discussed on this occasion, and Mr. Hudson stated that he was ready to pledge himself to make, along with the railway, a footway for general passage; but with respect to a horse and carriage-way, he had great doubt of its safety and practicability, and could not give any pledge on the subject, but that he and Mr. Robert Stephenson meant to give the matter further consideration."

From his association with the Greens' schemes Hudson expected that at least 60,000 pedestrians would use the bridge each week even if tolled at a penny[3]. He also knew that Robert Stephenson had incorporated a footpath relatively cheaply between the two tracks of a trussed cast iron bridge over the River Ouse on the York to Scarborough railway which was nearing completion[4]. Robert Stephenson's absence from the meeting and the other two engineers' apparent silence on the provision of a carriageway may have been in the hope that having agreed to provide a central station and guaranteed the bridge some concession to the railway promoters may have been forthcoming from the committee. The argument for the carriageway must have been put a lot more forcibly than the mere question in the report suggests for the very next day a letter was received by the chairman of the sub-committee and printed in full in the report:

> "MY DEAR SIR,
>
> In consequence of what passed at the meeting I had the honour of having with the Committee of the Corporation yesterday, on the subject of the bridge over the Tyne, proposed to be made by the Newcastle and Berwick Railway Company, I have had a consultation with Mr. Robert Stephenson this morning, and after hearing his views and explanations, I have no hesitation in saying that if the Council, expressing the opinion of the majority of the inhabitants of the town, shall desire it to be done, I will engage that the bridge shall be made applicable to the passage of horses, carriages, and foot-passengers, as well as railway carriages.

In accordance with what I proposed yesterday to the Committee, I will give directions that a clause shall be inserted in the Act (a copy of which will be sent for the perusal of the Corporation), by which the Newcastle and Berwick Railway Company shall be prevented from taking toll on any part of their line unless the bridge over the Tyne, and the passage of the railway through Newcastle, be completed within five years from the passing of the Act.

I am, &c.,

GEO. HUDSON."

He had achieved the committee's support, at some cost, for immediately after quoting the letter the report stated:

"We do not hesitate to recommend that Mr. Stephenson's line be assented to and supported by the Corporation, as the most desirable for the interests of the town.

Without entertaining the slightest doubt of Mr. Hudson's sincerity, and being satisfied that the clause proposed by him for securing the execution of the bridge over the Tyne and the line through the town will be effective, yet we think the public mind on the subject will be more completely set at rest if, by the same clause, the Company should be required to commence the bridge simultaneously with the works on the line of railway between Newcastle and Berwick, and proceed with all reasonable despatch in its completion. . . . In conclusion we beg to express our opinion that the proposed bridge over the Tyne be a stone structure; and we recommend this point be pressed upon the consideration of the promoters of the Newcastle and Berwick line".

After some argument the Stephenson line gained the support of the Town Council and the High Level Bridge, as we know it, passed its first hurdle towards Parliamentary approval and with no real opponents the Newcastle and Berwick Railway gained Royal Assent on 31st July 1845[5].

Provisions of the Act absolved the Newcastle and Darlington Junction Railway from its commitment to build a bridge under its 1844 Act on condition that the company paid £100,000 towards the cost of the High Level Bridge. The Act required the bridge to be constructed within four years of the passing of the Act for both rail and road traffic. It gave Newcastle and Gateshead councils powers to complete the bridge and to recover penalties from the company for failure to comply[6]. The road deck was opened six months after the deadline but as the railway company was acting in good faith no penalties were exacted.

As soon as the Act was passed the engineers could think about how they were to build the bridge. Unfortunately neither Robert Stephenson nor T. E. Harrison had time to present a paper on the bridge for discussion at the Institution of Civil Engineers and none of the subordinate engineers for the railway company or the contractors took up the task. This has deprived us of a record of a number of the decisions involved in designing the bridge, a summary of all the problems encountered during its construction and the many points that would have been raised by senior members of the engineering profession in the discussion that would have followed the presentation of the paper. A clear description of the bridge was written by Captain R. M. Laffan R.E. when he inspected it on behalf of the Commissioners of Railways for the Board of Trade on 11th August 1849[7]. Six years later a brief but lucid account of the bridge was written by Robert Stephenson for the *Encyclopaedia Britannica*[8]. A set of six drawings of the bridge made in 1858 and 1859 by Robert Hodgson (1817-77), the senior resident engineer of the Newcastle and Berwick, were presented to the Institution of Civil Engineers. They are beautifully prepared and give some details of the methods of construction. (Colour Plates VII and VIII)[9]. Railtrack archives also contain a large number of original drawings and contemporary newspapers give some indication of the progress of the works.

Decisions 1: Height, Site and Width
Some of the decisions were readily reached. The road and rails had to be at different levels to avoid a totally objectionable oblique level crossing or a convoluted descent to get the road below the railway at either one or other end of the bridge. Also the extra expense to provide almost double width river piers to carry parallel structures would not have found favour with the railway promoters.

Colour Plate VIa   John Wilson Carmichael used the engineering drawings of the High Level Bridge to produce this artist's impression before even the contracts had been let. This detail from it shows the Gateshead abutment and Nos. 1 and 2 spans. The major difference from the completed bridge is the small masonry arches shown over the footways in the piers. Reproduced by kind permission of the University of Newcastle upon Tyne.

Colour Plate VI b. A detail from one of John Storey's panoramic views, showing the High Level and Tyne Bridges. To the right of the latter is the tower of St. Mary's church, Gateshead, while the steep descent of the High Street and Bottle Bank towards the old bridge is quite evident. The open ground at the bottom right-hand corner is a portion of the former Brandling Junction terminus at Oakwellgate.   Laing Art Gallery.

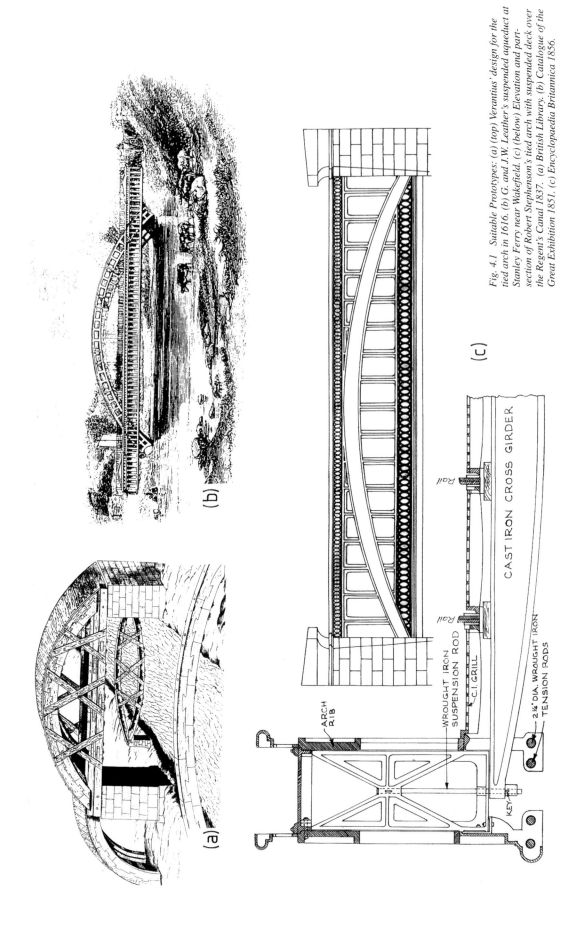

Fig. 4.1 Suitable Prototypes: (a) (top) Verantius' design for the tied arch in 1616. (b) G. and J.W. Leather's suspended aqueduct at Stanley Ferry near Wakefield. (c) (below) Elevation and part-section of Robert Stephenson's tied arch with suspended deck over the Regent's Canal 1837. (a) British Library. (b) Catalogue of the Great Exhibition 1851. (c) Encyclopaedia Britannica 1856.

The height of the rails on the bridge of almost 120ft. above ordnance datum was fixed by the level of the former Brandling Junction Railway in Gateshead. An easy falling gradient of around 1 in 260 over a long viaduct connected it with the Newcastle and North Shields Railway at Manors[10]. The Newcastle and Carlisle's final extension into Central required a climb of about half a mile at 1 in 96 which was a lot better than the 1 in 23 up the rope-worked Redheugh incline into Gateshead[11].

At the Parliamentary enquiry prior to the Railway Bill being proved, Robert Stephenson was asked about crossing Newcastle on a viaduct[12]. He replied that over Dean Street the extreme height would be 70ft. but that the average through the rest of the town would be 25 to 30ft. When asked: "Do you see nothing objectionable in crossing a town at that elevation?" he answered: "No, it has not been found by experience to be so". The Town Council had raised no objection to the levels being aware that to have lowered them to avoid the viaduct would have meant every street but Dean Street and Manor Chare would have a level crossing. The levels of the road deck of the bridge of approximately 96ft. above ordnance datum fitted in nicely with West Street, Gateshead and Collingwood and Mosley Streets, Newcastle. The position of the bridge next to the old arch bridge had been chosen by the Greens and endorsed by Hudson and the Stephensons. It gave almost equal radii for the tracks on each approach to the bridge of between 600 and 660ft. and again fitted into both townscapes[13].

The width of the bridge was determined by providing a reasonable carriageway of just over 20ft. and two 6ft. 2in. footways. These plus the inner arch rib thickness provided the exact width necessary for a three track railway on the top deck. If the road deck had not been required the railway company would, almost certainly, have opted for a two track bridge and then as traffic built up they would have added another two track structure alongside just as they did on the viaduct east of Central Station on the Newcastle and Berwick[14].

Decisions 2: Material and Basic Design of Superstructure
Newcastle's request for an all masonry structure was ruled out on grounds of cost, weight and the need to provide a double-deck superstructure. Weight was to be a very serious consideration in the design because of the difficult foundations below the river. Cast or wrought iron were the only sensible options for the superstructure as steel was only produced in very small quantities at that time.

Cast iron was first used for a major bridge in 1779 when the famous Ironbridge at Coalbrookdale was completed. Its span of 100ft. exceeded almost all the masonry bridges in Britain built before it[15]. By 1796 a cast iron bridge with a span of no less than 236ft. had been completed over the River Wear at Sunderland and it used only 260 tons of iron[16]. Improvements in the quality of iron and casting techniques meant that the strength, lightness, durability and rapid construction afforded by the material could be exploited. All the early cast iron bridges followed the obvious convention imposed on masonry bridges and supported their deck above a series of arch ribs which was satisfactory only as long as the deck and its approaches could be constructed high enough to give the necessary clearance between the arch and the watercourse below. Thomas Telford (1757-1834) ran into the clearance problem with the Admiralty when he proposed a 500ft. span cast iron arch over the Menai Strait in 1810. His only solution, at that time, to provide the required height over the whole span, was to replace the arch with a suspension bridge[17]. Telford gave the credit for solving the arch clearance problem to George Leather (1787-1870) a Leeds' engineer[18]. Leather's idea was to suspend the deck below the arch by wrought iron ties and his principle was used on early railway bridges by both Stephensons and later for the road deck of the High Level Bridge. The strength of cast iron and the validity of Leather's theory was very thoroughly proved when he and his son built the Stanley Ferry Aqueduct over the River Calder near Wakefield between 1836 and 1839 (Fig. 4.1). Two cast iron arch ribs each weighing 101 tons support by 70 slender wrought iron ties a 165ft. long cast iron trough weighing over 500 tons and containing 940 tons of water. It remained in service for 142 years[19].

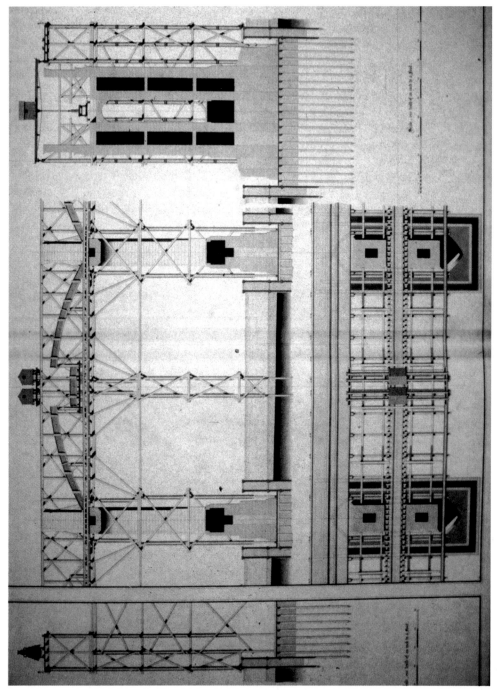

Colour Plate VII   Robert Hodgson's drawing showing the temporary viaduct scaffolding and elevated travelling cranes with a centre segment of one of the arch ribs being lifted into position. The voids within the piers are shown in black.   Photograph by Bill Fawcett by permission of I.C.E.

Colour Plate VIIIa   Robert Hodgson's cross-section through the top of a pier showing a travelling crane and the temporary viaduct alongside. Photograph by Bill Fawcett by permission of I.C.E.

Colour Plate VIII b. A detail from the drawing reproduced in Plate VII, showing the raising of the centre segment of one arch. Photograph by Bill Fawcett by permission of I.C.E.

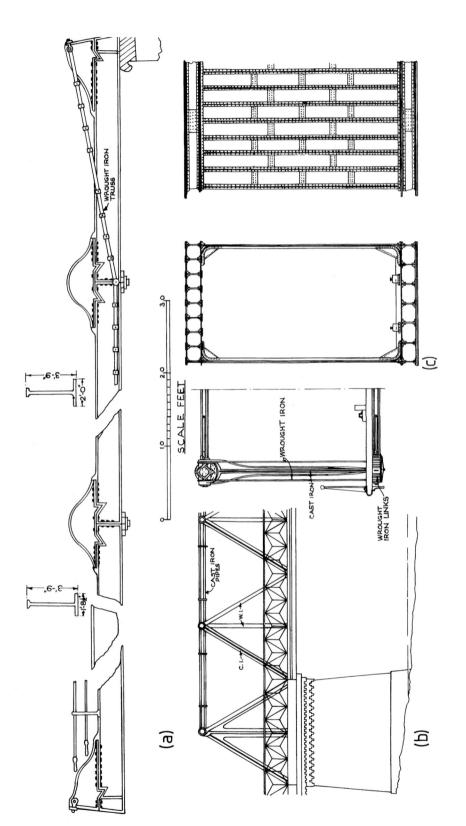

Fig. 4.2 Unsuitable Prototypes: (a) Not strong enough: the failed trussed girder of the Dee Bridge. (b) Not developed far enough: the lattice Warren girder as used at Newark Dyke needed another five years development before it was used very successfully by Kennard and Warren for the Crumlin Viaduct in South Wales. (c) Not adaptable enough: the need for a two deck structure and the poor ground conditions ruled out the use of the tubular girder over the Tyne. (a) Illustrated London News 1847. (b) Encyclopaedia Britannica 1856. (c) Tubular Bridges.

The theoretical design for a tied or bowstring arch probably went back to the beginning of the seventeenth century when a Croatian, Faustus Verantius (1551-1617) produced an illustration of a dovetailed timber arch tied by fishplated timber beams in his *Machinae novea* which was published in 1616[20] (Fig. 4.1). The first known tied iron arch in Britain was completed in 1820 for a road over the River Chelmer, near Chelmsford, to the designs of Ralph Dodd C.E. (c.1756-1822). A description in the letter in a contemporary journal appreciated perfectly that the tied arch ". . . has no lateral thrust or pressure and ... is certainly of the greatest importance in saving of expense where there is difficulty in getting a foundation."[21] Segmental arches with a relatively small rise from their springing to their crown produce considerably more horizontal thrust than a semi-circular arch with the same span and loading. The difficulty of building abutments and piers capable of resisting the thrust of large arches was eliminated by the use of chains or ties to resist their thrust. Both Stephensons had used this principle from the mid 1830s and it was to be of considerable importance in the design of the High Level Bridge[22].

Although cast iron had been established as a sound structural material for arched bridges at the time that the High Level Bridge was being built it was to fall into disrepute by being used beyond its practical limits for ordinary girder bridges. Cast iron is over five times as strong in compression as it is in tension and being hard and brittle it can snap without warning if subjected to excess tensile or shear stress. The maximum size for a sound casting was considered to be 40ft. and although large arches were successfully built up from a number of smaller castings problems arose when some engineers started to build up longer girder bridges by joining two or three cast iron beams together to save the additional cost of an arch. Since the early 1830s engineers had tried to relieve the tensile stress in the cast iron beams by attaching wrought iron trusses but not only was the theory not properly understood but the method of construction left a lot to be desired[23]. It was only a matter of time before a bridge of this type failed and it was to be the longest, constructed with 98ft. spans, that collapsed under a train on 24th May 1847, killing five people[24]. This bridge over the River Dee near Chester had been completed just seven months earlier under the direction of Robert Stephenson[25]. On the day of the accident he had supervised an additional depth of 5in. of ballast being spread over the deck. Luckily for posterity the accident did not finish his career (Fig. 4.2). The coroner's inquest and the Board of Trade accident investigation left a number of questions unanswered and a commission was appointed on 27th August 1847 to inquire into the application of iron to railway structures. Most of the senior civil engineers gave evidence and when the report was issued on 26th July 1849 (hereinafter referred to as the 1849 Report) it gave considerable insight into the theory and practice of bridge building at the time the High Level Bridge was being constructed[26]. Trussed girder bridges all over the country were strengthened but fortunately and correctly no legislation was recommended. Robert Stephenson spoke out strongly against any "legislative enactment" when giving evidence because had rules been made it could have stultified bridge design for decades[27].

During the eighteenth century processes had been developed to reduce the carbon content from around 4% in cast iron to less than 0.5% to produce a far more ductile material in reasonable quantities and patents had been taken out for the production of bars, angles and plates by rolling the improved quality malleable or wrought iron. Although wrought iron had been used in conjunction with cast iron in a number of early bridges, including the Stockton and Darlington Railway's 1825 bridge over the River Gaunless, it did not find favour for a complete bridge until the early 1840s. Reputedly it was first used to carry a road over the Polloc (sic) and Govan railway, near Glasgow with a span of just 31ft. 6in. in 1841. The six main box girders under the deck were filled with concrete; probably also the first time concrete had been used in a structural bridge member[28].

In the early 1840s even I. K. Brunel, who had completed the large hulls of the *S.S. Great Western* and *S.S. Great Britain* in wrought iron, preferred to use timber as an alternative to masonry, brick or occasionally cast iron for his bridges[29]. The reasons for not using wrought iron was due to some engineers' distrust of rivetting, the relatively small size of wrought iron plates then available and the higher cost. Writing in 1850 G. Drysdale Dempsey said the largest plates he knew were 10ft. 7in. by 5ft. 1in. and these were about twice the area of the biggest plates currently being used in the Britannia Tubular Bridge[30]. In 1845 when Robert Stephenson was making the preliminary designs for the High Level Bridge and the Britannia Bridge over the Menai Strait, intending them both to use cast iron arches, he came up against the same Admiralty

Colour Plate IX.   William Bell's contribution to the west end of Central Station. On the right is No. 1 Neville Street, built as the Revenue Accountant's office, to its left is the 1906 roofing over the west-end docks, fronted by a screen wall whose lunettes echo those of Dobson's original facade.   Bill Fawcett.

Colour Plate X   The much-extended hotel. On the left is Bell's 1890 addition with its stair-tower. On the right is Prosser's original 1862 block, raised by two floors and an attic but stripped of the incongruous canted bays seen in plate 6.5.

clearance requirements at the Menai as Telford had. Instead of considering suspending the rail deck from either normal or tied arches he went for a completely different solution that was to increase the span for a wrought iron bridge from 31ft. 6in. to nearly 460ft. in a decade. His idea was to build large tubes for the trains to travel through and he enlisted the help of William Fairbairn (1789-1874) and others to carry out calculations and experiments to find the best shape and size of tube to be used and to test thoroughly the properties of wrought iron. The results were the Britannia and Conway tubular bridges on the Chester and Holyhead railway and others elsewhere[31] (Fig. 4.2). Robert Stephenson took the tubular idea a stage further when he started to use smaller tubular, hollow or box main girders to carry the deck between them. The first was designed in July 1846 and completed in January 1847 to carry Chalk Farm Lane over the former London and Birmingham Railway (by now L.N.W.R.) near Camden[32]. An early bridge of this type was also used to cross West Street in Gateshead (Fig. 4.7).

Timber lattice bridges had been used on a number of railways and particularly in America and an idea being developed in Ireland in the early 1840s was to use wrought and cast iron in lattice main girders instead of wood[33]. Although this type of construction was to be used in many thousands of bridges in the future, including the King Edward Bridge over the Tyne, a number of engineers including Robert Stephenson, spoke out against it in the 1849 Report, because of the current problems caused by liveliness of the structure under loading[34]. At that time they were correct as when the Great Northern Railway completed a 249ft. span cast and wrought iron lattice bridge over Newark Dyke in 1852 it gained a reputation for lack of rigidity and had to be replaced in 1889[35] (Fig. 4.2); others in Ireland fared even less well[36].

From 1846 some engineers, including I. K. Brunel, started to build up arch ribs from numerous wrought iron plates and sections[37]. Excluding the rivets this method of construction used 20 to 30 times as many pieces of metal as would have been necessary with cast iron ribs[38]. Although cast iron is now regarded as an outdated and often derided material there is nothing to prevent an arch bridge on a railway being built of it today. After the Tay Bridge disaster of 1879 cast iron was prohibited on all *new* railway bridges *except when used in arches*[39].

On 1st October 1845 when the Newcastle and Berwick Board instructed T. E. Harrison to prepare plans for their bridges none of the uses of wrought iron had been developed far enough to be considered as an alternative to cast iron for the High Level Bridge. A tubular bridge might have been considered by Robert Stephenson but the distance between solid and reasonably shallow foundations would have given a span much larger than the Britannia Bridge. Also the need to support a carriageway below the railway did not fit in well with the tubular design concept. Tied or bowstring rigid cast iron arches supporting the railway above the ribs in the conventional manner and carrying a suspended road deck below them was really the only solution then available. The High Level Bridge was to be yet another "first" for the Stephensons in its use of the double decks.

Decisions 3: Span Piers and Foundations

There was still a major decision to be made before the detailed design of the bridge could start. What should the span be between the supporting piers? When the site was chosen the River Tyne had a maximum depth of just three feet at low tide and a width at high tide of between 515 and 520ft. Unfortunately for the bridge builders, earlier in its geological history, the river had cut a further 40 to 50ft. down through the rock below its 1844 bed level[40]. Subsequent rises in sea level, mainly due to climatic changes, had caused the river level also to rise and its bed had become silted up. The proximity of the old Tyne Bridge, downstream, had caused a further local build up of about 5ft. of silt[41]. From their preliminary site investigations the engineers knew that it would be necessary to drive long timber piles through the silt to the bedrock to obtain a sound base on which to build the masonry piers. The height from the bedrock to the superstructure was some 140ft. and to quote Captain Laffan "Such a foundation for so lofty a structure rendered it necessary that the whole design should be as light as consistent with safety"[42].

Before the Tyne Improvement Commission was set up by an Act of Parliament in 1850 Newcastle Corporation had the task of controlling the river with the Admiralty having the final say on any works affecting it. Clause 23 of the Newcastle and Berwick Act listed their conditions which included ". . . there be not more than Three Piers placed in the Bed of the River *Tyne* within High-water Mark,"[43]. Rather than going for larger spans and a heavier structure Robert Stephenson decided to accept the ruling and divide the river into four spans of 125ft. with three piers in the

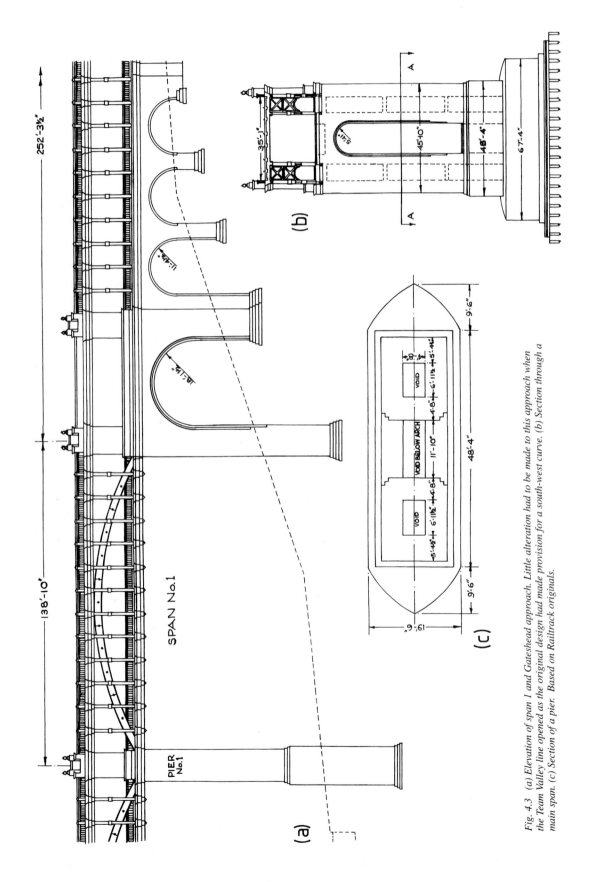

Fig. 4.3 (a) Elevation of span 1 and Gateshead approach. Little alteration had to be made to this approach when the Team Valley line opened as the original design had made provision for a south-west curve. (b) Section through a main span. (c) Section of a pier. Based on Railtrack originals.

water. He added an extra span on each side of the river to tie back to the land arches as it was considered too expensive to carry these masonry arches down to the edge of the river[44]. Even though the piers were made as light as possible the estimated weight and cost of each of them was 5000 tons and over £11,000. Almost two miles of an easy rural railway could have been built for a similar sum of money in the 1840s. On large structures the engineers had to consider economics as well as safety as considerable amounts of money could be wasted on unsound decisions.

A saving of £1,500 and 1,000 tons was made in the weight of each pier by the large arched openings and by leaving voids within the ashlar masonry on each side of them (Fig. 4.3)[45]. The voids were only filled with rubble, set in mortar, from the bottom of the piers to about 6ft. above high tide to prevent the ingress of water[46]. An injudicious mix of ashlar and rubble in its piers led to the spectacular collapse of Knaresborough Viaduct in 1848 and it had been the view of a number of senior engineers that providing the ashlar walls were thick enough to do their job it was much better to leave voids in piers than to fill them with rubble[47]. In 1851, when talking about the Royal Border Bridge, Robert Stephenson ". . . attached no importance whatever, as regards the stability of the bridge, to the rubble in the piers; it was like pouring so much sand down a chimney in order to add to its weight."[48] Another advantage was that the voids assisted the drying out of the slow setting lime mortar which could take months to reach its full strength[49].

When the span had been decided the precise position of the piers, which were numbered 1 to 5 from the Gateshead side, could be determined. Boreholes were taken on the proposed centre line of each pier to find the thickness and exact nature of the underlying material. The depth of the freestone was found to vary between 22ft at No. 1 pier to nearly 50ft at No. 5. The piles for Nos 3 and 4 piers would have to pass through over 30ft of wet sand "almost of the nature of quicksand" and other boreholes showed bands of gravel, clay or shale mixed with the sand[50]. It was decided to take the masonry foundation for No 1 pier down to 35ft below ground level to rest on the bedrock but each of the other piers had to be supported on 121 bearing piles, 12in square, and up to 50ft long[51].

Decision 4: Detailed Design of the Superstructure
Although the main parameters for the superstructure had been established the exact manner in which it was to be constructed had still to be decided. Robert Stephenson had a very good prototype in a bridge that he had built on the London and Birmingham, a decade earlier, over the Regent's Canal, about a mile from Euston station. It was the very first railway bridge to incorporate a tied cast iron arch and a suspended deck. It had a span of 50ft and carried two pairs of tracks of which one pair was intended for, but never used by, the Great Western Railway[52]. This bridge made a considerable impression at the time and was illustrated in Bourne and Bury/Ackermann prints also descriptions and engineering drawings of it appeared in a number of contemporary books. Francis Wishaw, writing in the early 1840s, attributes the design of the bridge to an assistant engineer, Mr Fox (later Sir Charles Fox 1810-1874), but it is certain that Fox was only producing detailed drawings of Stephenson's concept and the responsibility and the credit must go to Stephenson as Engineer-in-Chief[53]. There were no doubts about the authorship of the High Level Bridge as T. E. Harrison, who was known in the profession as "Honest Tom", made it quite clear in a letter dated 24th April 1846 "The plans have been prepared under my direction: the designs are *not mine* but my friend *Mr Robert Stephenson's*"[54].

The Regent's Canal bridge is shown in Fig. 4.1 and it would not tax the engineers' ingenuity to enlarge and adapt the design. The position of the cast iron bracings and the wrought iron suspension hangers between the arch ribs needed modifying to allow the footpath to be included on the High Level Bridge but for most of the design it was just a case of increasing the dimensions and adding the extra deck.

On the High Level Bridge the clearance between the road and rail decks was considerably more generous than was necessary and resulted from the need to keep the horizontal thrust to be taken by the tension chains within reasonable limits. The rise from the springing to the crown of the arch ribs was made 17ft 6in but a dimension of 12ft 6in would still have given adequate clearance for the road vehicles although the horizontal thrust would then have been increased by 40 per cent. The arch ribs which are 3ft 6in deep at their crown increase to 3ft 9in at their springing have 12in wide flanges; the thickness of the webs and flanges being 3in for the inner ribs and 2in for the outer ones. The ends of the ribs are specially adapted to accept the tension chains and to allow for the extra loading carried by the inner arches there are eight 7in by 1in

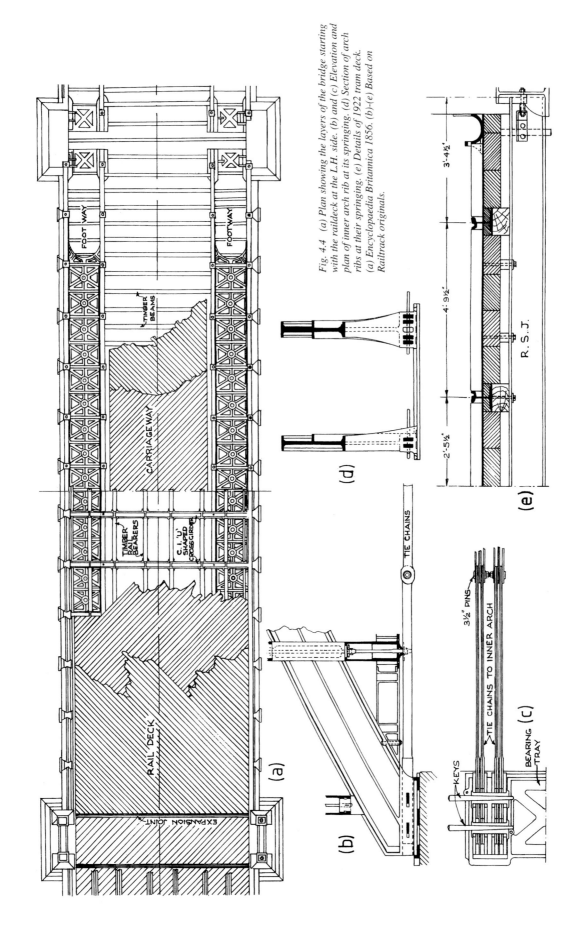

Fig. 4.4 (a) Plan showing the layers of the bridge starting with the raildeck at the L.H. side. (b) and (c) Elevation and plan of inner arch rib at its springing. (d) Section of arch ribs at their springing. (e) Details of 1922 tram deck. (a) Encyclopaedia Britannica 1856. (b)-(e) Based on Railtrack originals.

FOOT WAY

FOOTWAY

TIMBER BEAMS

CARRIAGE WAY

TIMBER RAIL BEARERS

C.I. 'U' SHAPED CROSSGIRDER

RAIL DECK

EXPANSION JOINT

(a)

(b)

TIE CHAINS

(d)

KEYS

3½ PINS

TIE CHAINS TO INNER ARCH

BEARING TRAY

(c)

3'-4½"

4'-9½"

2'-5½"

R.S.J.

(e)

chains against four for the outer. Each arch was cast in five sections and firmly bolted together and each pair is braced above the footpath with the cast iron frames (Fig. 4.4)

The rail deck is supported above the arches by twelve 14in square cast iron columns at 9ft 11in centres and for the sake of appearance and extra rigidity they continue down to the level of the road deck. Also the wrought iron suspension rods for the road, which are encased in the columns, extend not just below the arch but to the full height between the decks. This means that the arch ribs are interrupted at each point where the tension rods pass through them and this undesirable feature may explain why the arch ribs were made large enough to be stressed at less than one-fifth of the maximum permitted. Longitudinal trough girders 12in wide by 14½in deep are enlarged locally to 16in wide where they rest on the top of each hollow column. They in turn support, over the column centres, the transverse cast iron troughs which have six large "boxes" cast on each side to locate the ends of the 12in square longitudinal rail bearers. Two smaller "boxes" support the ends of 6in by 12in timbers carrying the edges of the decking (Fig. 4.5). The deck planking was 3in thick, tongued and jointed with hoop iron and laid diagonally in two courses which crossed each other at right angles[55]. A layer of patent felt was put in between the two layers and "the upper course was caulked and pitched with as much care as would be bestowed on a ship's bottom" said Robert Stephenson but there were still complaints from road users about water coming through![56]

The ends of the transverse timbers at 3ft 3in centres supporting the footways and the carriageway rested on the flanges of cast iron I section beams carried by the wrought iron suspension rods. The carriageway decking was again two layers of 3in diagonal planking but the paving was novel and patented by John Hosking the supervisor of the ironwork and decking. It consisted of 4½in wooden cubes from which ½in had been removed on four sides to half their depth. The top of the planking was covered with pitch then the blocks were dipped in hot pitch and laid tight up to each other. The grooves formed by the rebating of the sides were filled with broken stone and gravel and blinded with sand[57]. The footway planking was given a thin coating of lake asphalt but due to the work being carried out in the cold and damp of mid-winter it failed within five years and had to be renewed. The wooden planking was continued across the land arches but here there was a layer of concrete over 1ft thick immediately under the timber. The tension chains are supported at five points across each span below the I section girders. Matching cast iron parapets were provided for each deck with fascias below to cover such necessary but inelegant features as tension chains and girders.

Detailed drawings and contract documents could now be prepared based upon the decisions already taken.

Decision 5: The Selection of the Iron

It was very important that a consistently high quality of iron be used for the bridge. It was well known that iron produced from ores from different localities varied in strength and other characteristics but by the mid 1840s engineers and iron founders were only starting to realise the effects that small variations in carbon content and the presence of traces of other elements had on the performance of the iron[58]. It was the standard practice of the ironworks to produce a selection of qualities of iron to suit different uses. Engineers went a stage further and mixed iron from different works produced by different processes. When giving evidence for the 1849 Report, Robert Stephenson was asked "Have you never found that one iron has half as much strength again as another?" He replied ". . . you annihilate discrepancies of that kind by the mixture that all engineers stipulate for."[59] Earlier he had been asked "Can you give any opinion as to what mixture you prefer for large castings?" - "I cannot and do not think that any one can give a positive opinion on that point. For instance at Newcastle, at the erection of the High Level Bridge, I had a great number of experiments made with bars about 3ft long and an inch square, from, I should think, 50 different localities. I had them tested accurately, and although, in one or two cases, the anthracite iron from South Wales was the strongest, yet the difference was not so great as to make it an object for an engineer to run to any additional expenses: five, or six, or seven per cent probably is the range on one side or the other, from the medium of all irons in this country."[60] The experiments were conducted at Gateshead Ironworks soon after the contracts were let and the iron was tested singly and as mixtures. The mixture of the six irons selected contained a local one from Ridsdale, Northumberland. A description of Ridsdale iron making and details of the mixture of iron selected for the bridge are given in Appendix 2[61].

The wrought iron chains were made from best scrap iron and tested to 9 tons per square inch[62].

Land Purchase and Compensation

The Act allowed the company to purchase all the land and property necessary for the railway's construction. The demolition of the property needed to build the High Level Bridge and its approaches together with the viaduct from Central Station to Manors required 130 families in Gateshead and 650 in Newcastle to lose their homes[63]. Most of them were tenants and would only get small compensation but the owners of the property could demand the fair market price for their buildings. The right to arbitration was available to both the owners and the railway company but Hudson said it spoke much for the honour and integrity of the inhabitants that of the over 200 owners to be dealt with in only three or four instances were the terms offered by the company disputed[64]. One of these cases involved the creditors of a bankrupt glass works who were obviously out to reduce their losses at the expense of the railway[65]. The architect, John Dobson, was employed to carry out valuations and authorised to make payments on behalf of the company in some instances. The Newcastle and Berwick minutes record that Dobson was paid a total of £2,170 between 4th December 1846 and 9th March 1848 to disburse as compensation and tenant rights[66]. The spread of the dates indicates that some cases were not settled until well after the railway took possession of the site. A painting in the Laing Art Gallery, Newcastle by T. M. Richardson snr, even portrays workmen digging away for the foundations of the approach viaduct with substantial buildings still in the way.

The amount paid out for land and compensation for the whole project was £135,000; over one quarter of the total cost[67].

Contracts

As well as the High Level Bridge and its approaches the Newcastle and Berwick Act authorised the building of another 95 miles of main and branch lines which included 10 large viaducts and over 250 bridges. To produce the drawings, quantities and contract documents in a very short time must have required a skilled workforce of junior engineers, surveyors and draughtsmen. There are never any reports of their activities and no one ever says what a good job they did. From the surviving evidence on the Newcastle and Berwick it is apparent that they did their work very quickly and well and they must have been working in anticipation of the Act being passed as the 12½ mile Killingworth contract was let within a month of the Bill's approval; other sections followed rapidly. The large number of complex drawings and documents for the High Level Bridge and its approaches took nine months to finalise; the ironwork drawings are particularly detailed and must have taken a lot of skill to prepare[68].

The advertisements for the tenders for the masonry and ironwork appeared in national and local newspapers during June 1846 and the contracts were awarded in July and August[69]. In order to assist the contractors tendering for the ironwork, to visualize how the superstructure was to be built, a model of one span was available for viewing in London during the tender period and it was later to be used by the winning contractor to plan how to cast and erect the superstructure[70]. The main contractors for the ironwork were Hawks, Crawshay & Sons of Gateshead and they were assisted by John Abbot & Co. of Gateshead Park Works and Losh, Wilson and Bell of Walker Ironworks in the production of the castings. Their tender was accepted at £112,000. The contracts for the bridge piers and land arches and for the Newcastle Viaduct were won by John Rush and Benjamin Lawton of York for £94,000 and £82,500 respectively; this firm were already working on the Killingworth contract. The Gateshead approach viaduct was let to Wilson & Gibson of Newcastle for £9,861[71]. The total cost of the contracts at present day prices would be over £30 million. The contract documents contained this clause "No deviation from any of the provisions of this Contract Specification or Drawings will be permitted unless with the Sanction in writing of the Company's Principal Engineer". Robert Stephenson was probably fed up with people altering carefully thought out details to make it easier for them to complete their work[72].

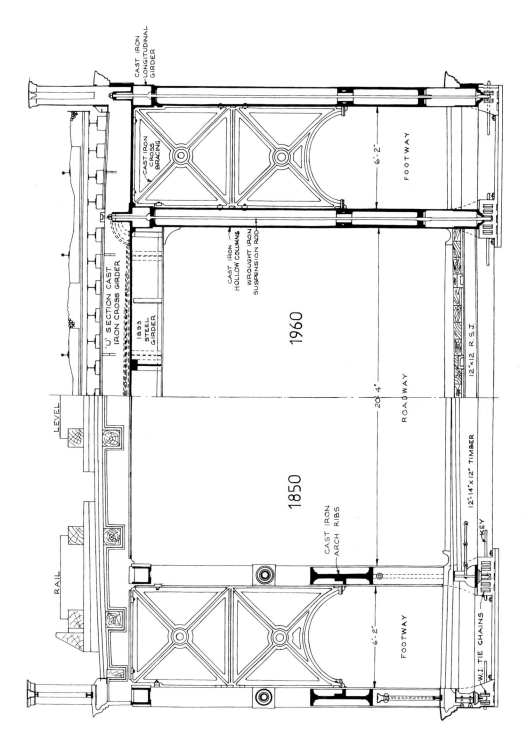

Fig. 4.5 Section of superstructure showing changes between 1850 and 1960. Based on Railtrack originals.

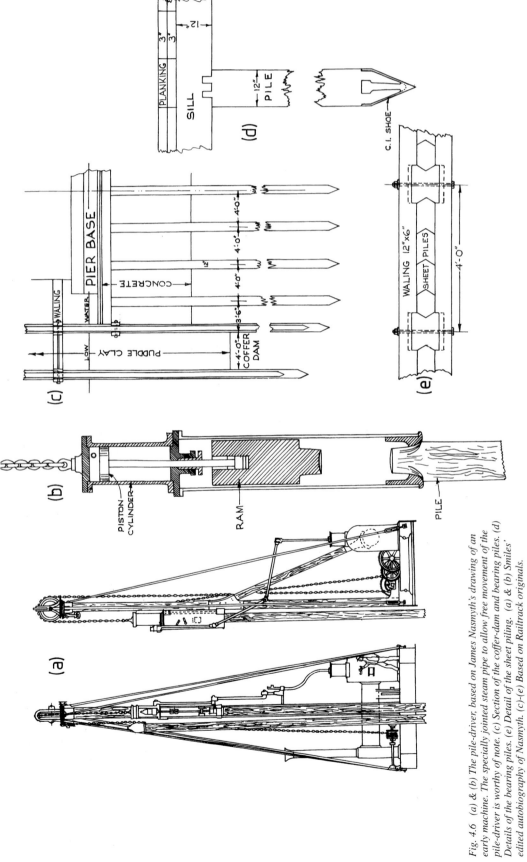

Fig. 4.6 (a) & (b) The pile-driver, based on James Nasmyth's drawing of an early machine. The specially jointed steam pipe to allow free movement of the pile-driver is worthy of note. (c) Section of the coffer-dam and bearing piles. (d) Details of the bearing piles. (e) Detail of the sheet piling. (a) & (b) Smiles' edited autobiography of Nasmyth. (c)-(e) Based on Railtrack originals.

Building the Bridge: Masonry

As soon as the chosen contractors were informed of their success they started very quickly to organise the manpower, equipment and materials necessary to complete their respective operations. The masonry contractors had to arrange the supply and transport of over 50,000 tons of stone from quarries up to 18 miles away. Land was rented on the river bank at Elswick and near Gateshead station for storing and shaping the stonework. The *Gateshead Observer* reported in November 1846 that there was already a large accumulation of stone near Greenesfield and tracks and cranes had been installed there to move the stone for the large numbers of masons employed to shape it ready for use in the piers and approaches to the bridge[73].

Before any work could start the property in the way of the line had to be demolished and 21 days' notice to quit was served on the owners and tenants at the beginning of August 1846[74]. The legality of this was doubted but it worked and the site clearance for the Newcastle approach was far enough advanced to enable the first masonry to be placed at its north end on 12th January 1847[75]. By March the clearance for the Newcastle to Manors viaduct was almost complete and the timber supports for the elevated travelling cranes, required to lift the masonry blocks, were being assembled on both approaches. This work went on day and night and it was in thick fog in the early hours of 23rd March that the first fatal accident occurred when a man was crushed by part of the temporary crane falling on him[76]. It was also in March that the masons got a wage increase from 26 shillings (£1.30) to 28 shillings (£1.40) per week but early in June, in an attempt to hold the contractors to ransom, they went on strike for 30 shillings per week[77]. They had to return to work without the rise and the ringleaders were not re-employed[78].

The stone for the bridge had to be hard and durable and it was selected from quarries at Heddon-on-the-Wall and Corbridge but a more local stone from Benton was considered good enough for the Newcastle to Manors viaduct[79]. The suitability of the lime and sand for the mortar and the way they were prepared and mixed was most important for the performance of the masonry. Normally local material was used but a selection from as far afield as Lyme Regis was used for the piers in an attempt to get the very best then available for the bridge[80].

The ground conditions for the land arches were worse than anticipated and contemporary accounts suggest that their foundations had to be taken deeper and wider causing considerable delays to the work[81]. The approaches and the piers were both ready by mid-1848 and the first ironwork was placed on 10th July 1848, possibly almost a year later than had first been envisaged[82]. The works for the rest of the railway were going very well as between 1st March and 1st July 1847 the Newcastle and Berwick was opened from Manors to Tweedmouth by means of temporary viaducts where the permanent structures still had to be completed[83]. At the time that the last section between Morpeth and Bilton (Alnmouth) was being opened Hudson announced that there would also be a temporary viaduct over the Tyne and a model of it and the scaffolding for the erection of the permanent one was to be seen at Hawks, Crawshay's works in August 1847[84]. The scaffolding for the tracks supporting the travelling cranes had been taken up to its full height by July 1848 and the temporary viaduct on the east side of the bridge was ceremoniously opened on 29th August[85] (colour plate VII). Normal traffic started running on 1st September and the final temporary viaduct over the Tweed, adjacent to the Royal Border Bridge, was opened on 10th October 1848 allowing trains to travel from London to Edinburgh for the first time. The celebration for the opening of the temporary viaduct over the Tyne was clouded by the fact that George Stephenson had died on 12th August and there was a proposal to name the permanent structure "Stephenson Bridge"[86].

Building the Bridge: Foundations

Back in 1846 there was still the challenge of the river foundations to be met before they could even think of temporary or permanent viaducts. Before any of the bearing piles could be driven coffer-dams were constructed around each of the three river piers and on the river side of No 5 pier. The internal dimensions of the coffer-dams were 76ft 6in by 29ft and they were formed by two rows of timber sheet piling set four feet apart. Each row was made up of 12in square timber king or gauge piles again four feet apart with 12in by 6in shaped timber sheeting between them (Fig. 4.6). The inner row of gauge piles was driven down to the bedrock or as far as the ordinary hand worked pile drivers could get them. The outer row was driven 16ft to 30ft below low water level and the timber sheeting a little less. The difference between high and low water at that time was 11ft 6in and the tops of the coffer-dams were finished just above high water level. The sand between the two rows of sheet piles was removed to a depth of about 16ft below low water and filled to above high water level with well rammed puddle clay in an attempt to make the coffer-dams watertight. The sand within the coffer-dams was then removed to a depth of 11ft 6in below low water level to make it easier to drive the bearing piles[87].

James Nasmyth (1808-1890) had designed a new steam pile-driver which had first been used at Devonport docks in 1845. It employed a 1½ ton ram that had a fall of 2ft 9in and was capable of delivering 60 to 70 blows per minute to the head of the pile[88]. On 19th March 1846 the committee of management of the York and Newcastle and Newcastle and Berwick decided "... to purchase a pile driving machine, including a small winding engine, for driving 48ft piles, from Nasmyth & Co at £1,150 for the High Level Bridge foundations". The winding engine was used to haul the next pile upright whilst the previous pile was being driven. Prior to the purchase of this machine the ram had to be laboriously raised by man, or at best, horsepower prior to each blow on the pile (Fig. 4.6).

A test pile was driven with the new machine on 24th April 1846 nearly four months before the contracts for the bridge were let[89]. Accounts of the test pile vary considerably. Captain Laffan writing in August 1849 says "I am informed that a weight of 103 tons was placed on the head of one pile and allowed to remain for four days"[90]. In late 1855 Robert Stephenson says "One of the foundation piles was tested with a load of 150 tons which was allowed to remain for several days"[91]. In the discussion following the presentation of his paper on Tyne Dock to the Institution of Civil engineers on 3rd May 1859 T. E. Harrison referring to the piling of the High Level Bridge states "... a dead weight of 100 tons of pig iron was placed on top of it and allowed to remain there for three months"[92]. At least they all agree that there was no settlement. According to a letter written by Harrison the driving of the test pile was only that "...some show of work should be made" to fulfil clause 26 of the Act which required work to commence within nine months i.e. by 30th April 1846. He proposed to continue piling prior to the contracts being let but unfortunately, from the delay point of view, this was not done[93].

The Nasmyth machine was used for driving all the bearing piles for the bridge which were at four feet centres. The hand operated machine still had to be used for auxiliary works and for the coffer-dams of the High Level Bridge and later for the Royal Border Bridge over the River Tweed. Samuel Smiles described the normal system prior to Nasmyth's invention with some derision. "By the old system, the pile was driven by a comparatively small mass of iron descending with great velocity from a considerable height - the velocity being in excess and the mass deficient, and calculated, like the momentum of a cannon-ball, rather for destructive than impulsive action"![94] (Sir) George Barclay Bruce (1821-1908), the resident engineer for the Royal Border Bridge, describes tests on the use of both machines and the results for the hand machine were not anything like as bad as Smiles describes. An ordinary ram weighing threequarters of a ton when allowed to drop 16ft had the same driving power per blow as the Nasmyth machine, under reasonable conditions, but the difference was that it took four minutes to wind the ram back for its next blow whereas the steam hammer could deliver 70 blows per minute! The average length of bearing pile driven per day on the Royal Border Bridge was between 29 and 50 feet[95]. When the first permanent bearing pile was driven for the High Level Bridge on 1st October 1846 it was reported "... a depth of 32ft was attained in four minutes"[96]. If only it had all been as easy as this the work of driving 20,000ft of piling including resetting the machine could have been completed within a month! Because the ground became more resistant with every pile driven the technique was to drive the centre piles first and then to work outwards. On the Royal Border Bridge they drove the bearing piles part of the way before forming the coffer-dams in an attempt to make the driving of each easier presumably after the difficulties experienced in the Tyne[97].

The Nasmyth pile-driving rig and its boiler were mounted on two flat bottomed boats or keels of the type which was then in common use on the Tyne and Wear to carry coal down river to ocean going vessels. In the first week, probably due to inexperience, the *Gateshead Observer* reported that the keels suffered "shipwreck" and needed "All hands at the pumps" but the pile-driver was soon in action again[98] One of the gauge piles that had been driven as far as it would go with the ordinary machine was driven, as an experiment, another 15ft with the steam pile-driver. The piles were memel or American rock elm and in several instances the heads of the latter burst into flames and burnt fiercely because of the heat generated by the rapid action of the ram of the machine[99]. The machine worked day and night except on occasions at high water.

In the *Encyclopaedia Britannica* for 1856 Robert Stephenson recounts the problems. "Many difficulties occurred in driving the piles which considerably retarded the progress of the work, and, among others, the peculiar effect of ebb and flow during the operation are worthy of note. At flood tide the sand became so hard as almost totally to resist the utmost efforts of driving, while at ebb the sand was quite loose, allowed of doing so with facility. It was therefore found necessary to abandon the driving on many occasions during high water. Another difficulty arose from the quicksands beneath the foundations. Although the piles were driven to rock bottom, the water forced its way up, baffling attempts to fill in between them; this however was remedied by using a concrete made of broken stone and Roman cement, which was continually thrown in until the bottom was found secure"[100]. Smiles adds, that before the concrete was considered "Chalk was thrown in in large quantities outside the piling, but without effect"[101] A factor that would have had a considerable bearing on the ingress of water was the scouring effect on the river bed caused by the narrowing of the channel by the coffer-dams; the depth in some places had increased by 7ft[102].

When the coffer-dams were eventually sealed from below and pumped out work could start on the timber bases to support the masonry piers. When driven to their limit the battered and charred tops of the piles would not all be at the same level and would need to be carefully cut off and morticed to take 12in. square memel crowns or sills. Except at the tapered ends there were seven piles in each transverse row and the sills connected each row across to horizontal walings on the inside of the coffer-dam (Fig. 4.6). The whole space within the coffer-dam to a depth of five feet below the top of the sills was filled with Roman cement concrete and with this concrete and the puddle clay the top of the coffer-dam would be now almost totally watertight even at high tide. Two courses of 3in planking were laid diagonally across the sills at right angles to each other and the foundation course of the ashlar for the piers was built directly on top of them[103]. During an examination for repair work, 70 years later, the memel sills and the planking of oak and rock elm were found to be in excellent condition even though no creosote had been used. The same examination showed that one of the iron tipped bearing piles had been driven straight through a 3ft diameter oak tree buried in the sand without damage but that the coffer-dam sheeting had shattered on contact with the tree[104].

On completion of the bridge the coffer-dams were left to protect the foundations and the sheet piles were cut off level with the bed of the river with a circular saw. The average weight carried by each of the bearing piles was over 50 tons with some carrying up to 70 tons[105].

Building the Bridge: Ironwork

The first thing that Hawks, Crawshay had to do was to get the samples of iron from all over Britain which Robert Stephenson required for testing. The tests were completed and the mixture to be used decided upon in February 1847 but meanwhile the pattern makers would have been hard at work making the many large and small wooden patterns needed to cast the ironwork and the first large casting was completed that month[106]. When each casting was produced it was proof tested with weights in excess of those it was likely to carry in service to guard against hidden flaws. Progress with the ironwork was very good and the first completed span was erected at the ironworks ready to be tested as a unit in July 1847 and according to Robert Hodgson each span was proof loaded with 700 tons. Confidence in iron bridges and in Robert Stephenson had declined since the collapse of the Dee Bridge eight weeks earlier and when Hudson turned up to view the completed span under test another 100 tons was added. When the weights were removed no ill effect could be detected in any of the parts and the *Gateshead Observer* commented "It has been thought necessary to expose the High Level Bridge to a somewhat unreasonable trial of its strength, for the satisfaction of the public mind; and the result has proved that the confidence of the architect and contractors was fully justified"[107]. After the test the span was taken apart and stored for a year awaiting assembly in the bridge itself. On 2nd March 1848 tenders had been accepted from Abbot & Co to build three cast iron bridges and for Robert Stephenson & Co. to build the new wrought iron box girder structure over West Street, Gateshead, to replace the existing "leaky tub"[108] (Fig. 4.7).

A foreman of Hawks, Crawshay, Thomas Taylor, was killed on 17th May 1848 when he fell from the Gateshead approach where he had been deciding how to strengthen the travelling cranes, used for the masonry, to carry the much heavier castings for the bridge arches[109]. This was the third and last death on the bridge as a man in charge of an old Dutch lugger used as a floating crane had been killed by a falling beam on 26th June 1847[110]. During the erection of the superstructure Hawks, Crawshay claimed to have spared no expense in providing "... the securest tackle and best constructed staging" for men working 120ft above the river[111]. In July and August 1849 two men had very lucky escapes. One a ubiquitous John Smith, a shipwright, was only

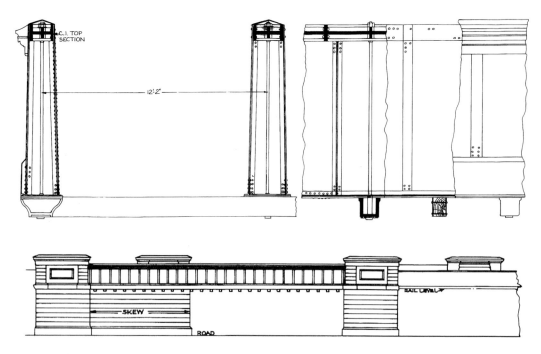

Fig. 4.7 Cross section and longitudinal section and elevation of the box girder bridge over West Street, Gateshead by Robert Stephenson. One girder of a similar bridge over Half Moon Lane survives. J. F. Addyman.

saved from plunging to his death when the seat of his trousers caught on a protruding nail. A Newcastle tailors, B. Joseph & Co, whose adverts comprising mainly of doggerel, often featuring the High Level Bridge, claimed that the life saving trousers were made by them but, somewhat embarrassingly, this was repudiated by Smith who wrote to the newspapers saying that he had bought them elsewhere![112] The 31st August 1849 was a bad day for accidents as two men suffered broken limbs and a third had a lucky escape when he managed to grab an extended beam after a (Hawks and Crawshay?) plank on which he was working broke under him[113].

The scaffolding and the arrangement of the travelling cranes and tracks and the method of erecting the arch ribs are shown in colourplates VII and VIII. The first section of the arch ribs, which weighed around 10 tons, was placed on 10th July 1848 and the bridge was visually intact from end to end when an arch rib for the northern river span was completed on 28th April 1849. The finishing touch to that span and the iron work was completed on 7th June 1849 when George Hawks J.P. of Hawks, Crawshay and Mayor of Gateshead, ceremoniously drove the last key in the tension chain at its Newcastle end[114]. When Captain Laffan inspected the bridge on behalf of the Commissioners of Railways for the Board of Trade on 11th August only the eastern track had been laid and during the afternoon he tested the bridge using a train of four tender locomotives and 18 wagons loaded with ballast weighing a total of 200 tons, which he ordered to pass backwards and forwards over it to try and detect, without much success, some deflection of the arches. From the heterogeneous collection of locomotives owned by the company they significantly selected one built by the firm that had provided the pile-driver and three of local manufacture: Nasmyth, Gaskell & Co, R. B. Longridge & Co, Robert Stephenson & Co and R. W. Hawthorn and Co. The train was considered to be "... a much greater weight in all probability than will ever pass along the bridge again" - little did they know! Captain Laffan passed the bridge without reservation and the first passenger train to cross it was the 9.30 am on Wednesday, 15th August[115].

Plate 4.4   The Illustrated London News printed this litho in its issue of 9 September 1848 to show the celebrations for the opening of the temporary viaduct over the Tyne. The timber structure depicted bears little resemblance to Robert Hodgson's drawings!

Plate 4.5   A lithograph from the Illustrated London News for 1 September 1849 showing the details seen from the road deck better than any photograph could.

Plate 4.6 The western footway resembling an early description which likened it to the aisle of a great cathedral. J. F. Mallon.

Plate 4.7 The iron work supporting the rail deck approaches with the additional 1893 columns under its centre line almost hidden by the original ones. J. F. Mallon.

Plate 4.8 The start of a span, showing the first joint in the arch ribs and the additional hangers provided in 1922 when the road deck was strengthened for the trams. J. F. Mallon.

The official opening by Queen Victoria occurred on her return from Scotland on 28th September 1849. *The Illustrated London News* reported "The arrangements for the reception of Her Majesty at Newcastle were upon a scale of much grandeur; and it may be doubted whether the Queen, in all her experience of Royal progress, has ever witnessed anything at all approaching the scene which she beheld when the train drew up on the summit of the High Level bridge. At a moderate estimate there could not have been less than 60,000 spectators immediately within view of the Royal carriage. In the centre of the bridge a platform of considerable dimensions, capable of accommodating 800 ladies and gentlemen, was erected at the west side, to which the parties were admitted by ticket; and immediately above where the Royal carriages stopped was a triumphal arch, profusely decorated with flowers and evergreens, and ornamented at the top with a large crown, having inscribed underneath, in conspicuous gilt letters, 'Welcome on both sides of the Tyne'.

"The Mayors and Corporations of Newcastle and Gateshead here presented addresses to Her Majesty, which were graciously received by the Queen and, after a few moments' delay, during which Her Majesty and the Prince Consort surveyed, with the greatest possible interest, the magnificent scene around and below them, the train proceeded, amid the cheers of the spectators, through Gateshead towards Darlington."[116]

It had been intended that both entrances to the road deck should have three magnificent triumphal masonry arches, which would be surmounted by a statue of George Stephenson at the Newcastle end, however, in the economies following Hudson's downfall they were deferred[117]. These had been designed by the engineers and, writing in 1855, Robert Stephenson was still hopeful that they would be completed but, unlike the *porte cochère* of Central Station they were never built[118].

George Hawks had travelled over the roadway in his carriage on 2nd August 1849 but it was not until 4th February 1850 that the road was completed[119]. Anyone with experience of modern block paving will appreciate how quickly it can be laid and the delays must have arisen from the slow supply of around 200,000 specially shaped wooden blocks required for the surface. There was a dispute between the railway company and Newcastle Corporation about making up the road from the bridge to St. Nicholas Square but as early as August 1847 Hudson had stated that he had made no commitment to do this work. The gas supply to light the bridge was not connected until February 1851 but whether this delay was the result of another dispute is not known[120].

The main dimensions of the bridge in imperial and metric units are given in Appendix 3 and it is of interest to note that the total weight of the ironwork only equalled that of the masonry of one pier making Newcastle's suggestion of an all masonry structure somewhat impractical. The total cost of the bridge and its immediate approaches was £243,000 giving an increase on the tender price of £37,000. The temporary viaduct cost £10,000 and the increased cost of the foundations and masonry came to £25,000; the ironwork exceeded the tender price by less than £2,000[121]. The cost of the bridge, approaches and Central Station totalling in excess of £600,000 must have made it one of the most expensive small pieces of railway infrastructure up to that time[122].

Recouping the Cost

The Newcastle and Berwick Act listed the maximum fares and tolls to be charged on the railway and the highway and toll houses and gates were permitted to be erected on the road at each end of the bridge. The road tolls allowed by the Act varied between 10d (4.2p) for a score of cattle and 1d (0.42p) for a pedestrian but only half of these two tolls were charged at the opening whereas charges for other animals and vehicles were reduced only by a lesser degree[123]. When the road was opened the hours of use were restricted from 5 am to 6 pm and it was not until June 1871 that notice was given that tolls would be collected day and night[124]. Clauses in the NER Act for 1869 allowed the company to vary the tolls and enforce penalties on those avoiding payment[125]. In 1871 a poster was printed (Fig. 4.8) stating that the full tolls permitted by the original Act would be charged but later the tolls were again reduced to ½d for pedestrians.

Plate 4.9 Horse trams waiting under St. Nicholas Street bridge about 1910. The wrought iron extension (nearest the camera) for the additional tracks provided in the early 1890s is almost identical in appearance to Abbot's cast iron original bridge to which it is attached. Newcastle City Libraries.

Plate 4.10 An atmospheric 1924 picture showing the problems of slow-moving horse drawn vehicles mixed with more modern transport. At this time 2,000 tram journeys were made each day over the bridge. Newcastle City Libraries.

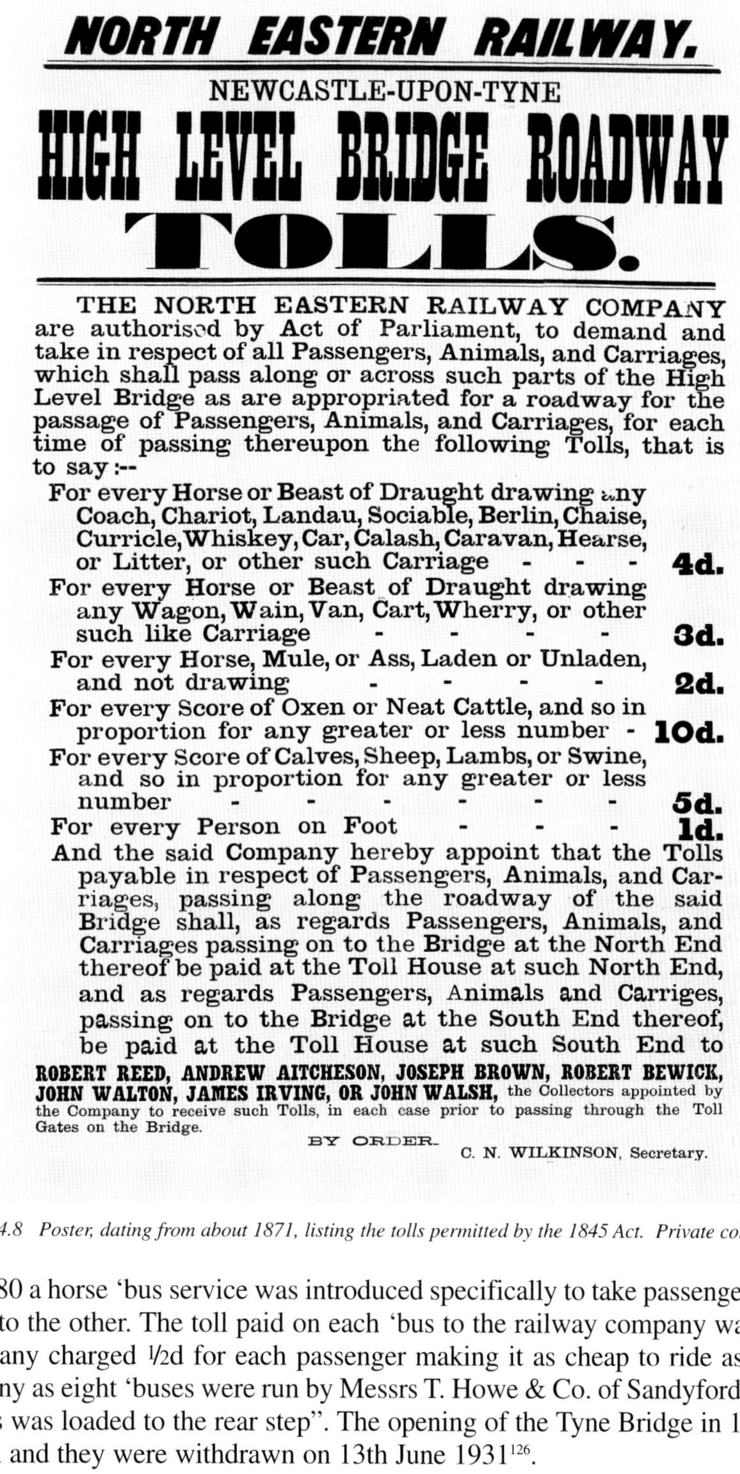

NORTH EASTERN RAILWAY.

NEWCASTLE-UPON-TYNE

HIGH LEVEL BRIDGE ROADWAY

TOLLS.

THE NORTH EASTERN RAILWAY COMPANY are authorised by Act of Parliament, to demand and take in respect of all Passengers, Animals, and Carriages, which shall pass along or across such parts of the High Level Bridge as are appropriated for a roadway for the passage of Passengers, Animals, and Carriages, for each time of passing thereupon the following Tolls, that is to say :--

For every Horse or Beast of Draught drawing any Coach, Chariot, Landau, Sociable, Berlin, Chaise, Curricle, Whiskey, Car, Calash, Caravan, Hearse, or Litter, or other such Carriage - - - **4d.**

For every Horse or Beast of Draught drawing any Wagon, Wain, Van, Cart, Wherry, or other such like Carriage - - - - **3d.**

For every Horse, Mule, or Ass, Laden or Unladen, and not drawing - - - - **2d.**

For every Score of Oxen or Neat Cattle, and so in proportion for any greater or less number - **10d.**

For every Score of Calves, Sheep, Lambs, or Swine, and so in proportion for any greater or less number - - - - - - **5d.**

For every Person on Foot - - - **1d.**

And the said Company hereby appoint that the Tolls payable in respect of Passengers, Animals, and Carriages, passing along the roadway of the said Bridge shall, as regards Passengers, Animals, and Carriages passing on to the Bridge at the North End thereof be paid at the Toll House at such North End, and as regards Passengers, Animals and Carriges, passing on to the Bridge at the South End thereof, be paid at the Toll House at such South End to

ROBERT REED, ANDREW AITCHESON, JOSEPH BROWN, ROBERT BEWICK, JOHN WALTON, JAMES IRVING, OR JOHN WALSH, the Collectors appointed by the Company to receive such Tolls, in each case prior to passing through the Toll Gates on the Bridge.

BY ORDER.

C. N. WILKINSON, Secretary.

Fig. 4.8 Poster, dating from about 1871, listing the tolls permitted by the 1845 Act. Private collection.

Around 1880 a horse 'bus service was introduced specifically to take passengers from one end of the bridge to the other. The toll paid on each 'bus to the railway company was 4d (1.7p) and the 'bus company charged ½d for each passenger making it as cheap to ride as it was to walk across. As many as eight 'buses were run by Messrs T. Howe & Co. of Sandyford and at one time "... every 'bus was loaded to the rear step". The opening of the Tyne Bridge in 1928 made them uneconomical and they were withdrawn on 13th June 1931[126].

In the early years of the twentieth century an extensive electric tram network had been built up on both banks of the Tyne but it was not until 1920 that agreement was reached making it possible to run them over the High Level Bridge. The Newcastle-upon-Tyne Corporation Act of 1920 paved the way and a further agreement dated 4th August 1920, with the NER, sorted out the financial arrangements. The last work that the NER did on the bridge before becoming part of the London & North Eastern Railway (LNER) was to rebuild and strengthen the road deck in the closing months of 1922 to make it ready for the trams to commence running in 1923. When the Tyne Bridge Act was passed in 1924 Newcastle Corporation agreed to pay the LNER a sum of £10,000 per annum in lieu of the £22,000 raised by the tolls on the trams agreed in 1920. The removal of all the tolls took place when Newcastle and Gateshead entered into an agreement with the LNER on 10th May 1937 to pay the company a sum of £160,000 and for Newcastle to take responsibility for the future maintenance of the road deck of the bridge[127].

Another source of extra revenue for the railway was its powers to charge an additional three miles on its train fares for crossing the High Level Bridge and, later, the King Edward Bridge[128]. The mileposts at the lineside take no account of the additional mileage but the railway must have been somewhat coy about it as even on some internal documents, such as gradient diagrams the distances are falsified to include the extra miles[129]. From 1925 the LNER published route charts for the use of its main line passengers called *On Either Side* which covered the journey from London to Scotland. The distance from King's Cross to Bensham is given correctly as 267 miles but to Newcastle, a little over 1¼ miles further, it is quoted at 271¼ instead of the correct 268¼ just in case any passenger could work out that he or she was being overcharged![130] Present day passengers need not worry as the extra charge was abolished in 1952[131].

Use: Rail

It was decided from the outset to have the eastern track for "up" or southbound traffic and the other two for "down" with the western one being reserved for goods traffic. In 1849, with an average of one train an hour using the bridge, the three tracks must have seemed a luxury but traffic was to build up very rapidly. After 1854 Gateshead engine shed was to be extended several times to accommodate the locomotives required to work the increasing number of trains and this brought its own problems as soon half the movements over the bridge were light engines going to work trains or returning for servicing and stabling[132]. When the part of the new main line using the Team Valley route was being built in the late 1860s T. E. Harrison proposed building a new bridge 700 yards upstream, almost on the line of the present King Edward Bridge[133]. However, at this time the NER was carrying out a more extensive railway construction programme than at any other period in its history and the idea was not pursued.

By the 1880s there were around 800 engine and train movements over the bridge each day, with inevitable delays, but the railway fought shy of the river crossing problem and gave priority to providing two additional tracks between Central Station and Heaton Junction and enlarging the station itself. When the quadrupling of the track was completed the light engine problem could have been alleviated by providing stabling at Heaton rather than at Gateshead shed. In 1893 Heaton was having a relatively small extension built and in 1894 the Board asked for estimates to be prepared for stabling another 132 or 154 engines there. This was not proceeded with even though it was taking up to one and a half hours from a locomotive leaving Gateshead shed to being attached to its train at Newcastle[134].

It was not until 1893 when the work at Newcastle and on the viaduct was well on its way to completion that the NER decided to consider the river crossing and other traffic needs around Newcastle. T. E. Harrison had died in 1888 and as there was no one in the NER organisation able to fill his shoes the Board asked the eminent consulting engineer, Sir John Wolfe Barry (1836-1918), son of the architect of the Houses of Parliament, to prepare schemes and estimates. His proposals were: widening the High Level Bridge to four or six tracks with two curving off towards Manors between the Castle and the Moot Hall; reviving T. E. Harrison's 1860s scheme; a line from the Team Valley at Bensham crossing the Tyne near the newly opened Dunston Staiths to join the Newcastle and Carlisle at Elswick; a lower Tyne crossing from Heaton to Pelaw; a tunnel from Elswick under Forth goods and Central Station to emerge between Manors and Heaton. None of these schemes raised any enthusiasm with the directors and the High Level Bridge widening implied a new superstructure and considerable disruption to traffic while the work was being carried out[135].

Five years were to elapse before the railway obtained Parliamentary Powers to build what has become known as the King Edward Bridge. The drawback with T. E. Harrison's original proposal was that in order to avoid the embarrassment of knocking down part of the brand new Forth goods warehouse the northern approach to the bridge had to be positioned too far east and would have resulted in a very cramped track layout at the west end of Central Station. Over 30 years later the scheme by T. E. Harrison's nephew, (Dr) Charles A. Harrison (1848-1916), sliced boldly through the warehouse. The bridge, which carries four tracks, has main spans of up to 300ft formed by double Warren steel trusses supported by granite piers; it was built by the Cleveland Bridge and Engineering Co, of Darlington and cost £500,000 excluding land and permanent way. The contracts were let on 6th March 1902 and it was formally opened by King Edward VII on 10th July 1906 and brought into use on 1st October 1906[136]. There were still 500 engine or train movements on the High Level Bridge after the new bridge was opened but the triangular track layouts at the south ends of each bridge allowed considerable operating flexibility also it was no longer necessary to reverse main line goods and passenger trains at Central Station.

In order to combat their declining suburban passenger figures caused by the introduction of the electric trams in 1901, the NER brought a new electric train service into use on North Tyneside in 1904. They had considered extending the service to Sunderland and South Shields and although the North Tyneside service was very successful it was not until 1938 that the first electric train ran over the High Level Bridge and then only on a service to South Shields. This service lasted for 25 years until it was replaced by diesel multiple units which were withdrawn on 1st June 1981 to allow the line to be converted for the use of the Tyne and Wear Metro. They reinstated the service to South Shields in 1984 using their own new Queen Elizabeth II Bridge over the Tyne leaving only the B.R. Sunderland and Middlesbrough local services over the High Level Bridge[137].

When the NER had drawn up plans for its York to Newcastle electrification in 1919 it did not propose to electrify any of the tracks over the High Level Bridge and when BR were considering their own East Coast Main Line scheme, nearly 70 years later, they also had doubts about running electric services over the bridge[138]. There was even a fleeting proposal to remove the tracks completely but as B.R. were then well advanced with their £1.5 million refurbishing programme and would still have to retain the whole structure for the road traffic this idea was dropped[139]. They went ahead with a 1983 proposal for two well spaced tracks and got the permission of the Royal Fine Arts Commission to erect specially designed electrification masts on the centre line of each pier[140]. The East Coast electric services started to run from Newcastle in June 1991 and the High Level Bridge is used by the main line electrics in emergencies or during maintenance works on the King Edward Bridge but main line diesel services regularly use it.

Use: Road
The railway's impact was immediate: within four days of the opening of the Heaton to Tweedmouth section the last mail coach on the Great North Road ran on 5th July 1847[141]; later at the opening of the temporary viaduct over the Tyne, the Stephensons' friend, Nicholas Wood said "In one concern in which I was connected they had, yesterday, about 39 horses employed in carting coke across the Tyne. This day that labour and expense has been suspended"[142]. Robert Stephenson quotes that the cost of the conveyance of passengers and merchandise across the old Tyne bridge had reached the enormous sum of £1,000 per week[143]. The success of the railway goes some way towards explaining why the road tolls for 1853 and 1854 only amounted to £2,000 and £2,700 respectively.

A deterrent to using the new bridge may have been the unmade-up state of the Newcastle approach road. The railway, and some of the more fair minded councillors, felt that as the company had paid for the bridge the Corporation should finance the approaches. It was estimated that £18,000 was needed for the work and the NER agreed to pay half as they considered the improvement would be advantageous to them. On 15th December 1854 they agreed that if the tolls exceeded £2,700 per annum threequarters of the excess should be paid to the Corporation until the sum reached £9,000 and interest at 4 per cent should be paid from the time that Newcastle incurred the expenditure. The NER paid off the £9,000 plus £2,054 interest by the mid 1860s which seems to indicate a healthy increase in the tolls after the road improvements.

Despite the opening of the Redheugh Bridge in 1871 the tolls on the High Level continued to rise and, by 1878, were estimated to have reached over £20,000 per annum. As the cost of the bridge had been more than paid off this led to an unsuccessful attempt to get the tolls removed.[144]

An indication of the use of the bridge prior to the Tyne Bridge being built is given in the figures for 1924 resulting from the 1920 agreement for the trams. By this the Corporation had to pay ½d for every passenger carried over the bridge and the LNER had to refund 2d for every tram. The total raised was £28,000 and the rebate was £6,000[145] suggesting that 1,000 trams ran daily in each direction carrying an average of 19 passengers - no wonder there was a desperate need for a new bridge! Although not anything like as busy as in the 1920s the High Level Bridge still continues to provide a useful link in the modern roads system of Tyneside.

Plate 4.11 The King Edward Bridge under construction about 1905. The tower at the Gateshead end is one of two supporting a cableway 1,520 ft long capable of carrying 10 tons. It was used by the contractors to handle nearly 24,000 tons of material and equipment during the construction of the bridge. National Railway Museum, Crown Copyright.

Plate 4.12 The approach from King Edward Bridge to Central Station cutting through the Forth Goods Station, probably pictured in 1959 during the changeover to colour light signalling which closed the career of No. 3 signalbox, whose gable is seen just left of centre. Straight ahead is the former Royal Infirmary, opened in 1752 and resembling a country house of the period. This was replaced by the Royal Victoria Infirmary at the beginning of the twentieth century and the building was near the end of its life when photographed. Hugh Murray collection.

Plate 4.13 A litho showing the much-admired Dean Street arch. It was sympathetically widened on its north side to carry two additional tracks in the early 1890s. Private collection.

Plate 4.14 The 1866 fire in Brown's corn mill showing its closeness to the High Level Bridge. The structure in the foreground is the temporary replacement for Robert Mylne's Tyne Bridge and it remained in use for nearly ten years awaiting completion of the swing bridge by J. F. Ure and W. G. Armstrong. Private collection.

Fire!

The most exciting incident in the life of the bridge happened on Sunday, 24th June 1866 when a tall, well stocked corn mill adjacent to the east side of No 5 pier caught fire. The fire was discovered before eight o'clock in the morning but within little over an hour the whole building was ablaze and soon its roof collapsed allowing the flames to reach the inaccessible underside of the roadway of the bridge. By mid morning there was real danger as the mill and its contents were far from either being consumed by the fire or being extinguished by the efforts of all the local fire brigades. The river's fire fighting vessel and the railway's own from Tyne Dock were both called to the scene but were able to do nothing for the bridge. About 100 railwaymen from Gateshead works and elsewhere were employed in an attempt to stop the fire spreading to all the road deck and they were set on, with picks and crowbars, to try and rip up the strong timbers of the decking to provide fire breaks. The panic was understandable because a little under 12 years earlier an explosion in a burning chemical warehouse in Gateshead had carried the fire across the river and caused an even larger blaze in Newcastle. Every local railway official from the permanent way inspector to the accountant seems to have been given orders and even Benjamin Lawton, one of the original contractors, made his valuable experience available. John Bourne, the divisional civil engineer, was summoned by telegraph from Penshaw and T. E. Harrison had to commandeer a special train from London.

It was not until two o'clock that hoses were positioned to play on to the burning decking from the roofs of warehouses on the west side of the bridge and within two hours the danger was over. It was thought that the masonry and ironwork of the bridge might be damaged, and the train service, which had been suspended at nine o'clock on Sunday morning, was not allowed to resume until after the engineers had carried out a detailed examination on Monday and passed the railway as safe. By Wednesday the west side footpath had been restored and pedestrians were allowed to use it. The estimated damage to the bridge was between £2,000 and £3,000 but it was covered by insurance. The mill was replaced by the less flammable fish market[146].

Maintenance: Foundations

In the mid 1860s, even though it was still possible to walk from the Gateshead side to a sand bank between Nos 2 and 3 piers, deep holes had been scoured on the upstream side of each of the river piers and this led T. E. Harrison to modify and strengthen the coffer-dams[147]. Forewarned by this scouring the engineers were concerned that the dredging of the channels, after the swing-bridge was completed in 1876, may affect the bridge foundations so they took soundings and plotted profiles of the river bed between the piers, about every seven years, in order to be assured that nothing untoward was happening[148]. About the end of the nineteenth century the river had been dredged to a depth of between 27 and 30ft below low water for the battleships that Messrs Armstrong, Whitworth were building at their Elswick works upstream of the bridge. To make it easier for these large vessels the channel between Nos 2 and 3 piers was chosen for widening and in 1906 it was agreed to cut away part of the swing-bridge jetty which surrounded No 3 pier and to remove the outer row of the coffer-dam on the north side of No 2 pier. Although the work was approved by C. A. Harrison the cynic might say that the alacrity with which it was carried out, without much thought for the consequences, may have derived from the fact that Lord Armstrong, a director of the company, had recently become a director of the North Eastern Railway. By 1911 they were having misgivings about No 2 pier even though a superficial examination did not show anything too serious. However, in 1915 it was decided to make a detailed examination using a diver and the report showed that the remaining sheet piling, on the north side, was out of line and had gaps in it; also soft mud had replaced some of the original sand between the bearing piles. As remedial work would have required narrowing the channel it was decided to postpone it until after the war in case a major naval engagement required urgent repairs to large vessels[149]. Measurements taken in June 1917 indicated that No 2 pier was almost 2in out of plumb but it was not until 1919 that repair work could begin[150].

A coffer-dam of steel sheet piling extending between 25 and 32 feet below low water was constructed around No 2 pier and made watertight. It was hoped that the mud could have been stabilised with cement grout but unfortunately this did not work. The only alternative was to underpin the pier by means of headings within the coffer-dam below the base of the original Roman cement concrete. Beside the new sheet piling, on the north side of the pier, the mud was found to extend to about 12ft below the underside of the old concrete but it sloped steeply upwards to fade out roughly at the east-west centre line of the pier. Being aware that the weight carried by the piles was over 6,500 tons the underpinning had to be done very carefully to ensure that the remaining sand around them was not destabilised by the operation. The concrete work for the underpinning was taken 12ft below the existing concrete at the north side and 8ft at the south and was done in 31 separate sections. The steel coffer-dam was left in situ and capped with a concrete apron extending above the base course of the masonry of the pier. At the same time examinations were carried out on Nos 3 and 4 piers but as the former was protected by the swing-bridge jetty no work was required. On No 4 pier it was found that sand mixed with mud appeared only on the south side of the foundation to a depth of 3 or 4 feet but to make sure that there was no further deterioration a permanent steel coffer-dam varying from 18 to 32 feet was driven between the inner and outer rows of the original one. All the work was carried out by Sir William Arrol & Co, the builders of the Forth Bridge, between June 1919 and April 1921. As there was no way of pre-measuring the work to be done the contract was awarded on a time-and-material basis and the cost came to just under £39,000. The 1906 alterations had been paid for by Armstrong, Whitworth but there is no mention of them paying for the remedial work[151].

Maintenance: Superstructure

Even during the construction of the bridge the weight of a passenger locomotive had increased from around 25 tons to almost 40 tons as the recently merged York, Newcastle and Berwick company ordered the larger engines to allow it to run a fast and efficient service on its new 150 mile long main line. By 1890 locomotive weights had increased to over 80 tons and the 160 ton Pacifics arrived in the 1920s. During the withdrawal of steam locomotives in the 1960s, bogie tank wagons weighing 100 tons were coming into use and these were capable of imposing a live load of 300 tons per track per span. Fortunately the High Level Bridge, like many others of its era, was able to carry loads far beyond those even dreamt of at the time of its completion and not a lot needed to be done to it to carry the extra weights. In 1890 it was decided to support the cast iron cross girders carrying the rail deck with steel box girders under the main spans. Where the approach spans curve away from the road the cross girders were supported, at mid span, by new columns but elsewhere they had to wait another 95 years for extra support.

In 1879 the whole of the timber work for the rail deck was due for its first replacement and new rail bearers of pitch pine and decking of Kyanized St Petersburg deals were used. This work was carried out within nine months in 1880 and although the flooring was again specially covered with felt and the joints sealed with oakum and marine glue it still leaked. Defeat was admitted and a timber canopy was put above each footway to deflect the drips from the unhappy pedestrians[152]. By 1898 having withstood nearly 50 years of iron shod wheels and horses' hoofs, the original roadway was in a very dilapidated condition as the asphalt which had been laid on top of the original block flooring had worn through in many places and large pools of water were forming. The transverse beams and decking were renewed in the same materials as the rail deck and the paving was Jarrah hardwood blocks. Two years earlier the footway supports had been renewed and a new concrete surface laid[153].

In 1922 the whole carriageway had to be strengthened to allow the trams to run and the type of construction is shown in Fig 4.4. The cast iron longitudinal girders were retained but two additional steel suspension rods were fitted from the inner arch ribs between each pair of columns. The road had to be closed for five weeks during November and December 1922 to allow the new steel beams, decking and tram lines to be installed. The work was again carried out by Arrols who also fitted the inspection cradles under the road deck of each span at the same time[154]. After the responsibility for the maintenance of the road surface was taken over by Newcastle in 1937 the railway company still retained the right to impose weight limits on vehicles and a 9 ton total weight and 6 ton axle weight was agreed[155]. In 1967 the vehicle limit was raised to 10 tons and rough estimates were prepared for lifting the limit to over 20 tons but when the figure arrived at exceeded £2 million the idea was not pursued[156].

Between 1955 and 1959 the timber rail deck was finally replaced by a steel trough deck carried on 21 longitudinal rolled steel joists and the original waybeam track was replaced by conventional ballasted track[157] (Fig 4.5). The addition of about 150 tons of stone ballast per span, on a 110 year old cast iron structure caused concern in some quarters but unlike the infamous Dee Bridge, mentioned earlier, this great old bridge could take it![158]

In 1968 British Rail employed a firm of consultant civil engineers to report on the condition and strength of the structure. A detailed inspection was made and load tests were carried out in December 1968 by using two Class 40 locomotives each weighing 133 tons and a 26 ton road vehicle. These were moved about the bridge and 100 electrical resistance gauges were used to measure the strain at various points on the bridge. Not surprisingly the results indicated that "... the behaviour of the structure was very complex"[159]. Following the report BR carried out minor repairs, did their own load tests and inspection and set up a more stringent annual inspection procedure. In 1983 it was decided to do an updated analysis of the bridge using the latest computer technology and to carry out a very thorough examination by B.R. staff. The analysis suggested that the weight limit for road vehicles, except 'buses and fire engines, should be lowered from 10 tons to 7.5 tons and to retain the existing axle loading on the rail deck the middle track should be removed and the remaining two tracks placed at 15ft centres[160]. The inspection particularly wanted to find out the condition of the original suspension rods and whether the 1893 steel cross girders were correctly supporting the original cast iron ones. The rods which are hidden in the columns were examined by means of an endoscope and were found to be in good condition. The fastenings for the steel girders were carefully assessed and in some cases tightened up but on the approach spans where they had never existed replicas of the previous beams were installed within a rolling programme of repairs which had started in 1982 and was to carry on until 1991. This included the repair or replacement of the rotted timber or corroded steelwork and a complete renewal of the drainage system. Visual improvements included the removal of the now rotten footway canopies and the additional railings and mesh screens at railway level also the replacement of one third of the damaged cast iron balustrade and newel capping together with repairs to the cast iron fascias[161].

In 1950, because of its unique character, the bridge had been classified as a Grade 1 listed structure by the Department of the Environment and although this meant that special consent had to be obtained to carry out work on it grants could be obtained for improvements to its appearance. The work carried out between 1982 and 1991 cost almost £1.5 million and grants totalling £300,000 were made by English Heritage and the Railway Heritage Trust also the local authorities contributed over £100,000[162].

At the time of writing (1999) the one thing that remains outstanding is the repainting of the structure which is estimated to cost over £500,000[163]. When the bridge was built it was painted stone colour but by 1859 it had become so badly stained by the smoky atmosphere that the directors decided to surrender to the inevitable and paint it black[164]. Analysis of the paint samples indicate that it has been painted grey for more than half its life and there are some arguments about the colour to be used for its next repaint[165].

In February 1999 consultants started another appraisal of the bridge and this is scheduled to take up to 18 months[166]. Since 1849 various attempts have been made to assess it starting with Captain Laffan's report. He used a theoretical live load of 520 tons and an incorrect dead weight for a span of 700 tons (which was 60 tons below the actual weight). In 1920 the NER load-tested a span with 781 tons and measured stresses of 0.85 tons per sq. in. for the arch ribs and 1.1 tons per sq. in. for the chains giving results of a half and one-sixth respectively of those calculated for the smaller loads in 1849[167]. In October 1935 the LNER used an impossible figure of 1740 tons for the live load and multiplied the stresses achieved by the NER by 3.13 to prove that both the arches and chains were well within their permitted maximum stresses. On the same sheet of paper they also used conventional calculations to prove that the chains would be overstressed by this theoretical loading![168] The load tests in the late 1960s did not give any cause for concern but the analysis of 1983 suggested a more cautious approach to the loading to be applied to both decks of the venerable structure[169]. Using the latest techniques it is to be hoped that the current assessment will be able to give a realistic and reassuring prognosis for the bridge's next 150 years.

Plate 4.15. The north abutment and arch over the Close, looking east. The damage to the balustrade capping and the less-than-elegant railings, mesh screens and signals are visible above the rail deck prior to the 1982 to 1991 refurbishing programme. Bill Fawcett.

Plate 5.1 An early photograph of Central Station, looking west along what was probably the main-line arrival platform. Note the gas lights bracketed out from the roof columns and springing from the second line of railings. The west end screens can be seen, together with the glazing below them in the southern roof span, which served as the YNB carriage shed. The four-wheeled carriages have a very short wheelbase and bear a greater resemblance to road vehicles than to modern railway carriages. National Railway Museum, Crown Copyright.

Chapter 5

NEWCASTLE CENTRAL STATION

BILL FAWCETT

Introduction

Newcastle Central is one of the great achievements of the Railway Age. Like the High Level Bridge it spans the often arbitrary boundary between Architecture and Engineering, and the office range and trainshed link two eras in evolution. The former evokes in a more practical form the grandeur and symbolism of Hardwicke's vanished Euston portico, the first gateway to the North, while beckoning towards the monumental Beaux-Arts neo-classicism of Charles McKim's Pennsylvania Railroad Station - another lost masterpiece. The trainshed can be regarded as a precursor of the great arched station halls yet it is at least as much an apotheosis of the Euston style of roof.

Before considering the design in detail, it is useful to look in outline at the original construction period when delays and changes in direction caused a radical alteration to its implementation. We left the story of Central Station in Chapter 1 at the meeting in January 1845 when Hudson finally capitulated to the demands of the Newcastle & Carlisle Railway and agreed to take part in the construction of a joint station on a site spanning the two locations previously selected by the smaller company, at the Forth and Spital. At this stage the N&C was reliant for engineering expertise on the limited experience of Peter Tate, and so it was left for Hudson to procure a provisional plan for the station and send it to that company. Soon after, the Newcastle & Darlington Junction Railway shareholders, at their half-yearly meeting on 4 February, agreed to subscribe half the costs of building the High Level Bridge and the Hudsonian portion of the new station. Meanwhile the N&C got plans sorted out for an extension of its line a distance of half a mile from the temporary terminus at Railway Street to the Forth.

Plate 5.2 The N&C viaduct leading to Central Station. The bridge over Forth Banks was rebuilt in connection with making the approaches to the King Edward Bridge. The gardens on the right were those of the Infirmary.

An Act for this was obtained in 1846 and the line was rapidly completed, even though most of it was on a low sandstone viaduct of 44 arches, culminating in an ornamental cast-iron girder bridge across Forth Banks. On 15 February 1847 it was inspected for the Board of Trade by Captain Coddington, who referred to the viaduct, now seldom noticed and with unusual forethought built for 3 tracks, as a 'substantial and very handsome structure' and gave his assent to the running of passenger services[1]. East of Forth Banks the company had already formed a level area at the height required for the permanent station and erected on this temporary buildings and platforms, to which passenger trains were transferred from 1 March[2]. Unfortunately for the Newcastle & Carlisle, Hudson was operating to a somewhat different timescale and it was to be a further four years before they could move next door into their permanent quarters in the joint station - on 1 January 1851.

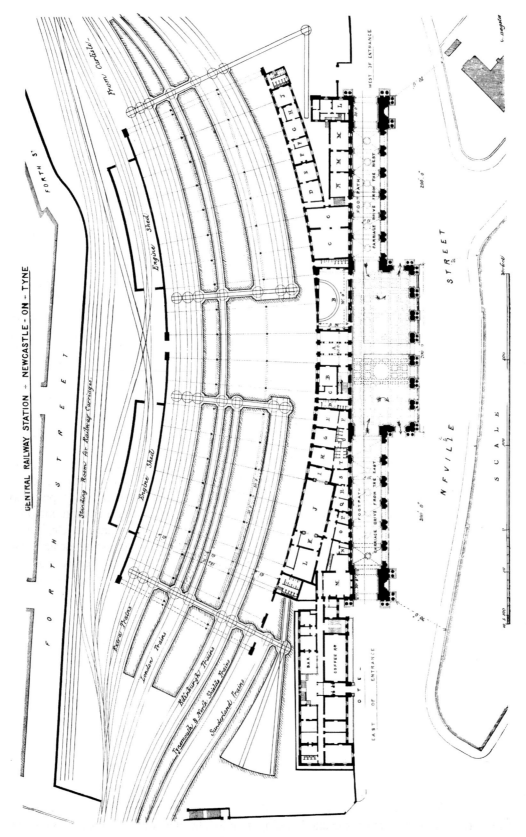

Fig. 5.1 John Dobson's plan of the layout of Central Station, published in the Civil Engineer & Architect's Journal in December 1848.

With the Act for the line to Berwick only being obtained in 1845 and completion of the High Level Bridge required within four years, Hudson could defer a new station until 1849. Indeed, there must still remain a doubt as to whether he really intended to redeem his pledge regarding the Newcastle station. On 17 February 1846 the N&C Board, having heard nothing from Hudson, approached him again and six days later, at a Newcastle & Berwick Board meeting on 23 February, John Dobson was formally appointed architect for the joint station. Dobson had, in a sense, been inherited from the Newcastle & Carlisle, both as their preferred choice in this role and as the designer of their final Tyne Bridge scheme with its double-decker option foreshadowing Stephenson's High Level Bridge, but he was also the acknowledged leader of the architectural profession in the area.

Dobson also won the lucrative task of conducting property valuations and negotiations for the sites of both station and bridge, but Hudson did not forget his debt to the Greens, whose Tyne Bridge scheme he had earlier adopted. Their reward was to design all buildings on the Newcastle & Berwick from just beyond Manors to the terminus at Tweedmouth. The outcome was a sequence of handsome station houses by Benjamin Green in the 'Jacobethan' style which had been popularised in small country houses by architects such as William Burn. Another local man, Thomas Moore, of Sunderland, was called on to design a handsome Greek Revival terminus at Monkwearmouth. The only person who may have felt displaced was G.T. Andrews, but he remained responsible for the buildings of Hudson's York-based companies south of the Tyne and was comforted with the task of designing a new station and hotel for Hull.

The layout of Central Station, in terms of tracks and platforms, was determined by T.E. Harrison and Robert Stephenson, in consultation with the Carlisle Railway's Peter Tate. The result can be seen in a plan published by Dobson in 1848 (Fig. 5.1). This shows the curve necessary to link the Gateshead and Carlisle lines, which determined the whole character of the building, and the surprising number of through platforms originally conceived, given that the station was essentially two termini placed back to back - with little through running of passenger carriages between the Carlisle line and other railways. These requirements, together with some siding space for the accommodation of carriages under cover, probably led to the conception of a trainshed roofed in three spans of sixty feet, then considered (by Charles Fox at least) to be a sensibly economic maximum span for a Euston truss roof.

For Dobson, despite his already-distinguished career, this was the chance of a lifetime. The Carlisle directors were keen to create a notable civic ornament, complementing Grainger's New Town, while secure in the knowledge that their contribution to its cost would be only about a quarter of the total. Hudson had a record of investing in fine buildings on his railways, partly to enhance his own prestige, and once converted to the necessity of the Central Station could be relied on to endorse an ambitious scheme and find the money needed to finance it. On 1 June 1846 Dobson explained his plans to the Carlisle directors, while on 18 August his design was approved by the Newcastle & Darlington Junction Board with instructions to prepare working drawings[3,4]. Thereafter the Carlisle directors took a back seat, delegating the management of the project to Hudson and his associates.

It should have been possible to advertise for tenders for the construction of the station in the Autumn of 1846, with a prospect of completion in 1848, by which time the High Level Bridge might well have been ready had it not been for the problems with piling. A further delay occurred, however, due partly to an alteration in the site but also arising from legal difficulties over land transfers between the Newcastle Town Council and the railways, which led to a suit in Chancery, which was not resolved until 25 January 1847[5], shortly after the first advertisement had been placed for contractors[6].

Tenders were required by 9 a.m. on 22 February 1847, an hour before the Newcastle & Berwick Railway directors were due to meet. In the event no decision was minuted regarding the station contract, which was deferred for almost 6 months until 7 August when it was let to MacKay & Blackstock for the considerable sum of £92,000[7]. These contractors were already well known to the company, constructing several portions of the line including the Royal Border Bridge at Berwick. Although the contract details are not known, it will have included the clearance of the very large station site and building it up to a level as well as construction of the platforms and station offices. The trainshed ironwork and roofing and internal plastering of the office building were reserved to later specialist contracts. No reason is recorded for this further delay, though the February tenders may have proved unexpectedly costly. What is known is that

Newcastle Corporation was not in favour with Hudson at this time, having ungratefully chosen to endorse a rival scheme for a new main line from the south along the Team Valley in preference to one promoted by his York & Newcastle Railway[8]. Perhaps the delay in starting work on the station was therefore both prudent for Hudson's cash-flow and a mark of his resentment.

At first work proceeded steadily, progress with the clearance of existing buildings being reported in September 1847[9]. The level platform for the structure, with its retaining wall to Forth Street at the rear, must have been well advanced by March 1848, when *Herapath's Railway Journal* reported a start on the foundations of the station building, but the contractors were still engaged on these in July, the first purchases of ashlar stone for the walls above ground being recorded shortly afterwards[10]. Progress continued to be slow, however, and on 13 February 1849 Hudson threatened to take the work out of the hands of MacKay & Blackstock unless they employed within ten days such additional workmen as the directors deemed necessary[11]. This is his last recorded act in relation to Central Station. The general economic climate had been deteriorating since Autumn 1847 and Hudson was now viewed by some shareholders in a more critical light - leading to the appointment of the York Newcastle & Berwick Railway Committee of Investigation in February 1849. Hudson's subsequent downfall was spectacular, and he never witnessed the formal opening of either the station or the High Level Bridge.

Once open to scrutiny the YNB's finances proved to be quite strained, thus it was under the critical eye of the Committee of Investigation that the Board proceeded with the completion of Central Station, letting the contract for the trainshed ironwork to John Abbot & Company of Gateshead and that for its glass to John Gibson of Newcastle[12]. Dobson had already made unspecified modifications to the design of the trainshed, reducing its cost from £12,000 to £10,000, but the main area where economies could be achieved was in the station frontage where a gigantic arcade, 600 feet long, was intended but had so far made little progress. Work on this was suspended, much to the chagrin of the Newcastle & Carlisle Railway whose finances were perfectly healthy, but whose position was rather uncertain[13]. Hudson had taken a lease of their line from 1 July 1848 on behalf of the YNB, which now took advantage of this to divert the contractors' efforts on to its part of the station, leaving the Carlisle end to languish. The YNB shareholders, however, repudiated the Hudson lease, restoring to the Carlisle Board its freedom of action.

In addition, the YNB decided to break its administrative ties with York, making its home in Newcastle, and deferring a large hotel originally intended at the east end of the station. Dobson was called on to revise his designs to include extensive offices and introduce a few hotel rooms into the main building as well - an interim measure pending the eventual construction of the separate hotel block. In the course of this he produced a revised scheme for the station frontage, to culminate in a somewhat reduced portico still costing £10,000. The Carlisle directors tried hard to persuade the YNB to accept this, John Clayton suggesting that £2,000 of the cost might be obtained from Newcastle Corporation to support such a civic improvement, but the YNB Board felt this would be very hard to sell to their hard-pressed shareholders[14]. So the portico and hotel building were omitted until the North Eastern Railway came to complete the project in 1863.

At the beginning of September 1849 the *Newcastle Journal* reported that Abbot's workmen had begun the erection of the trainshed. Almost five months later Dobson reported that half this structure together with the office roof above the rooms flanking the main entrance would shortly be completed[15]. The revisions had further delayed the scheme but the trainshed proceeded well ahead of the offices and was able to provide a fitting venue for a celebratory banquet to Robert Stephenson in his homeland on the evening of 31 July 1850[16]. The formal climax came on Thursday 29 August when Queen Victoria and Prince Albert opened the station during their progress north to holiday on Deeside. The opening day was declared a public holiday in Newcastle, and the railway directors recouped some of the costs of entertaining the royal party by selling viewing places, not just on the special stands erected inside the trainshed but also beside the tracks at the east end and on the High Level Bridge[17]. Later that same day Stephenson's Royal Border Bridge across the Tweed enjoyed its royal opening, though it was already in use. The following day YNB services were diverted into Central Station and Greenesfield Station closed.

Plate 5.3 A sublime essay in curves. The station concourse looking east in 1900-01 during the changeover from gas to electric lighting. The elaborate gas standard next to the entrance appears in one of Dobson's original illustrations; the roundel above depicts a young Queen Victoria. The NER has done little to harm the appearance of Dobson's office range - even the ingenious curved signs above the doors attempt to be sympathetic, though one wouldn't like them back. Newcastle City Libraries.

Victoria and Albert saw only the specially decorated interior of the trainshed and a few rooms fitted up for their use, although to make up for this they were presented with a book of watercolour drawings of the building, prepared by Dobson. Most of the office range was still far from complete, and even when the Newcastle & Carlisle moved in on 1 January 1851, much remained to be done - the drawings for the main refreshment room are dated March 1851 and the scaffolding was not finally away from the front of the building until the beginning of September; upon the revealing of the facade the *Newcastle Journal* pronounced that, even without the portico, it was 'the best railway station in the world'[18]

The Site
The original site of the station and its approach lines is overlaid on Thomas Oliver's 1830 map in Figure 1.3. The western and northern boundaries are those of the present station, but the site was later extended to the south and east, entailing a completely new alignment for Forth Street. Most of the site was open ground, although houses had to be demolished along Forth Street and near the Spital. One casualty was a section of the medieval town wall, together with the Spital and Denton Towers; other notable losses were the guild halls of the Bricklayers, on the eastern approach to the station, and Barber-Surgeons, on the route to Manors. Dobson designed replacement buildings at the request of both guilds, a sign of the times being that the Barber-Surgeons relocated from the town centre to the western suburbs (at Victoria Street)[19].

A spacious setting for the station frontage is provided by Neville Street, the idea for which originated about 1835 as an extension of Collingwood Street to link the town centre with Scotswood Road and the cattle market, which had been resited to the west side of the Forth. By the autumn of 1838 site acquisition for the street was well in hand and it was becoming more important as part of the access to the Newcastle & Carlisle Railway's intended temporary station at Railway Street[20]. Uncertainty over the location of a permanent station blighted development along the street but in 1845 the joint station was settled to be on its south side. An initiative from the council's Town Improvement Committee led to an enlargement of the station site, possibly to provide space for Dobson's arcade and portico, and a diversion of Neville Street to the north was agreed in September 1846[21] although the contract for this was delayed until 15 March 1848, when it was let to to MacKay & Blackstock,[22].

The Design of the Trainshed

Although the trainshed was the last part of the station to be commenced, it is convenient to describe this structure first, together with the context in which it was designed.

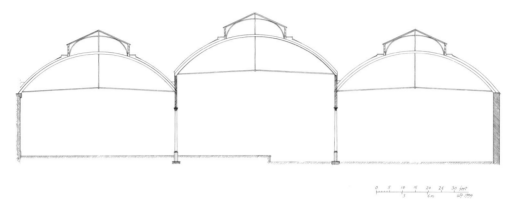

Fig. 5.2   Section through the original trainshed, looking east. Note the arched ribs supporting the skylight/ventilators - these were replaced by an angular design in the nineteen-sixties. Bill Fawcett.

The trainshed shares with Richard Turner's Liverpool Lime Street (discussed later) the distinction of having been the first to have been designed and built in Britain employing curved wrought-iron ribs to support an arched roof. It is in three spans of approximately 60 feet each, supported on the sandstone rear wall of the station offices, another such wall at the rear of the shed and concealed wooden trusses carried by two lines of cast-iron columns, which also provide the drainage for the valley gutters. (Figs. 5.2 & 5.3) The tall, slender columns carry delicate, semi-elliptical cast-iron arches formed by two open spandrel panels bolted together at the apex of each arch, and the timber truss runs immediately above these. The central roof span is carried on top of the truss, which is concealed by panelling, and the flanking spans spring at the base of the truss, their ribs being hung from it in such a way as to direct most of the load away from the cast-iron arches and down onto the columns.

The iron ribs have an I-shaped section and follow a segment of a circle, tied at the ends and from the crown of the arch by wrought-iron rods. The ribs were clad originally with timber planks running along the length of the roof, covered by some form of sheeting whose joints can be seen in Plate 6.1. This may have been a thin galvanised iron sheet (the roof being too large to permit the expense of using lead) but soon proved unsatisfactory, dry rot being reported in 1864[23]. The roof was reclad with slates on new planking in 1876[24]. Along the centre of each span was a glass skylight, raised on wooden louvres to ventilate smoke and steam and supported by a curved wrought-iron rib.

The main ribs posed a problem in that their section was too large to readily permit being rolled as a straight I-beam and then bent to the required curve (the technique used by Richard Turner). Thus they are fabricated from segments of wrought-iron plate, with L-sections riveted on to form the top and bottom flanges. Because of the restricted size of plate then available, the wastage involved in cutting the segmental sections for the web would have been very costly. Dobson, speaking in 1859, gave the impression that this could have led to a different roof design having to be adopted - possibly the simple Euston truss - but the problem was solved by Thomas Charlton, who was Hawks Crawshay's engineering foreman on the High Level Bridge contract[25,26]. Charlton developed a rolling mill using bevelled rollers; at their wide end the surface speed of the rollers is greater than at their narrow end so drawing the rolled sheet out faster along one edge than the other and naturally producing a segmental shape. Dobson estimated the resulting saving as £1,400, a very significant amount in the context of a total ironwork cost of £10,000 (with this saving) for the entire roof.

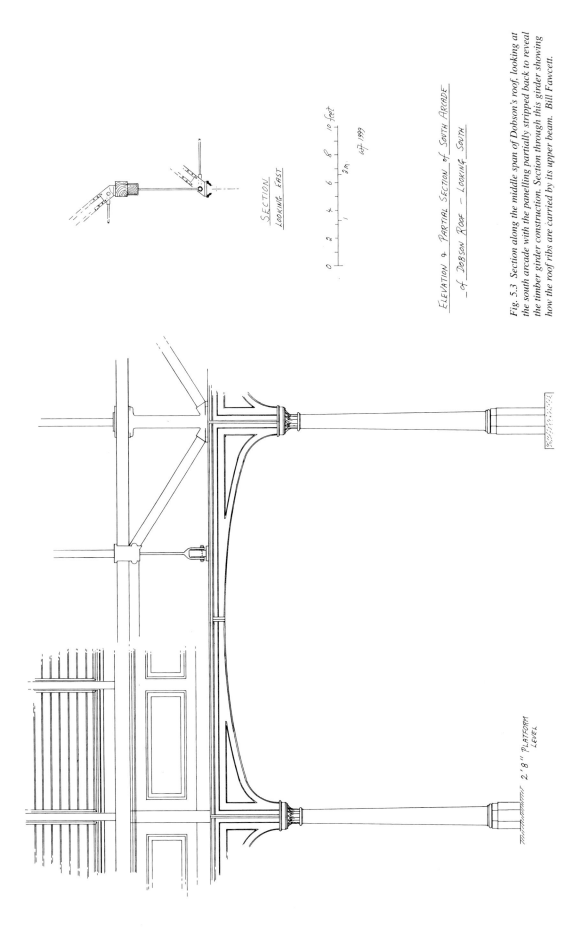

SECTION
LOOKING EAST

0   2   4   6   8   10 feet
        0m

bf 1999

ELEVATION & PARTIAL SECTION of SOUTH ARCADE
— of DOBSON ROOF — LOOKING SOUTH

Fig. 5.3 Section along the middle span of Dobson's roof, looking at the south arcade with the panelling partially stripped back to reveal the timber girder construction. Section through this girder showing how the roof ribs are carried by its upper beam. Bill Fawcett.

2' 8" PLATFORM LEVEL

Plate 5.4 The east end of Central Station, showing the original end-screens and, in the background, the rear of the hotel block constructed in 1862. The engine, No. 365, is typical of Edward Fletcher's later passenger locomotives and was constructed at Gateshead Works. This photograph was probably taken soon after its completion in August 1880. The engine was scrapped at Darlington in January 1920, having run 1,024,994 miles. Ken Hoole collection.

At both ends of the roof the arched tympani were filled by simple glazed wooden screens above very flat semi-elliptical arches, probably a very much drawn-out version of the cast-iron interior arcades, springing from pilasters on the sides of the end columns of each row.

The Context and Significance of the Trainshed

Trainsheds originated as a means of housing railway carriages when they were not in use and protecting them from interference and from the weather. The earliest was that added to the Liverpool & Manchester Railway's Crown Street terminus in Liverpool at the end of 1830[27]. It used wooden trusses as did the earliest stations of any substance in North-East England, the termini of the Leeds & Selby Railway, opened in September 1834[28].

By the eighteen-forties trainsheds with pitched roofs carried on the light wrought-iron Euston truss had become common, Greenesfield Station, described in Chapter 2, being a very good example of the type. Arched roofs had, however, made at least two appearances on the British railway scene. One was the North Shields station roof, using laminated timber arches and illustrated in Fig. 5.4. The other was a curious trainshed at Shoreditch, the London terminus of the Eastern Counties Railway[29]. Designed by that company's Engineer-in Chief, John Braithwaite, the structure is contemporary with Greenesfield Station and foreshadows in some ways Newcastle Central.

The Shoreditch roof (Plate 5.5) was in three segmental arched spans, the middle one raised above the others, the valleys being borne on cast-iron arcades with semi-elliptical arches. The spans, however, were narrow - a central span of only 36 feet being flanked by ones of 20 feet 6 inches, allowing the use of a structural system much simpler than that employed at Newcastle. There were no ribs; instead the roof was simply formed of thin sheets of corrugated iron bent to the appropriate curve and riveted together. Though ingenious it was viewed as a rather dark and unattractive place but, particularly given that Hudson had become chairman of the Eastern Counties in 1845, is likely to have been studied by Dobson. An inspiration for his eventual use of tied-arch ribs may, of course, be the High Level Bridge itself.

Plate 5.5 A Christmas train at the Shoreditch terminus of the Eastern Counties Railway. The view is slightly deceptive, in that the roof span directly ahead was barely 6 metres wide. Illustrated London News 21 December 1850.

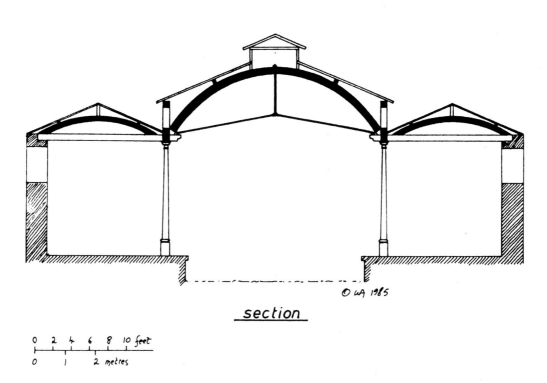

section

0 2 4 6 8 10 feet
0   1   2 metres

Fig. 5.4 A section through the trainshed of John & Benjamin Green's station at North Shields. The roof covered approximately 135 feet of platform and its aisles provided an extensive waiting area. The columns were perilously close to the platform edge, as in many of Brunel's smaller trainsheds. It was replaced by a single-span Dobson-style roof in 1888, while this in turn was demolished some years before the line was taken over by the Tyne & Wear Metro. Bill Fawcett.

The nave and aisles form of roof, with a visual focus provided by a raised central span, also has its predecessor in Dobson's own work. The commercial heart of Richard Grainger's development of central Newcastle was the provision of indoor market halls in a block extending from Grainger Street to Clayton Street. Dobson apparently designed the halls of the Grainger Market, which opened in 1835, though not the external facades. The largest interior is that of the Vegetable Market, which now strongly resembles a railway station, its 57 feet breadth being covered by a tall arched roof on lattice girders. This replaced Dobson's original roof, which was destroyed by fire in 1901 (Plate 5.6). That had narrow side aisles marked off by slender cast-iron columns bearing a wooden 'trussed purlin', as Dobson chose to call it, which elevated the trusses of the main, central span. Both the concept and the design of the trussed purlin closely anticipate his Central Station roof, with the same use of wrought-iron rods to pull the load of the aisle roofs up to the tops of the diagonal braces which then direct it down towards the columns.

Plate 5.6 The original Vegetable Market within the Grainger Markets, showing Dobson's use of 'trussed purlins' in a way that anticipates his Central Station design. Private collection.

Dobson's trainshed marked a watershed in station design. Prior to this elegant roofs had been created by practitioners such as G.T. Andrews, using the Euston truss in a trainshed integrated with the remainder of a station building. All too often, however, the trainshed and offices had been treated as disparate parts - a showy facade frequently concealing a trainshed without a sense of focus let alone the slightest hint of the spatial grandeur which is so apparent at Newcastle. Indeed railways had previously contributed little to architecture conceived as an enclosure of public space. By contrast, as early as 1807 Francois-Joseph Belanger had begun the replacement of the wooden dome at the Halle au Ble in Paris with one using cast-iron ribs to span a diameter of 108 feet[30]. Nearer home, Joseph Paxton had constructed a majestic conservatory for the Duke of Devonshire at Chatsworth from 1836 to 1841. The 'Great Stove' was fully glazed using Paxton's patent ridge-and-furrow glazing and had a central arched span of 70 feet using laminated timber arches springing from cast-iron galleries borne by cast-iron columns[31]. For some years buildings like these eclipsed the achievements of the railways and even while Central Station was under construction another building was underway which was to be equally influential.

In 1844 Kennedy and Vernon, of Liverpool, secured a patent for a system of iron shipbuilding making extensive use of deck-beams: rolled iron sections with a broad flange at one end of the web and a bulbous head at the other[32]. The deck-beams themselves were not patented and were taken up by a leading ironfounder, Richard Turner of the Hammersmith Ironworks in Dublin. In collaboration with Decimus Burton he used them for the arch ribs of the Palm House at the Royal

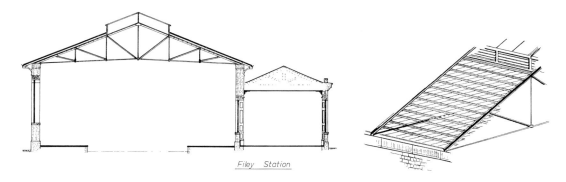

Fig. 5.5 A typical 'Euston' truss. Filey Station, in Yorkshire, designed by G.T. Andrews and opened in 1846. Bill Fawcett.

Botanic Gardens, at Kew, begun in 1845 and completed in 1848 with a central pavilion similar in profile to Chatsworth but having a span between columns of only 50 feet[33]. To provide rigidity he linked the ribs with hollow, cast-iron tubes, serving as purlins and post-tensioned by wrought-iron rods inside[34]. The deck-beams were supplied to Turner in 12 feet lengths which he welded together in a furnace before shaping them into the curve required.

Plate 5.7 Kew Gardens: the Palm House by Richard Turner and Decimus Burton. Illustrated London News.

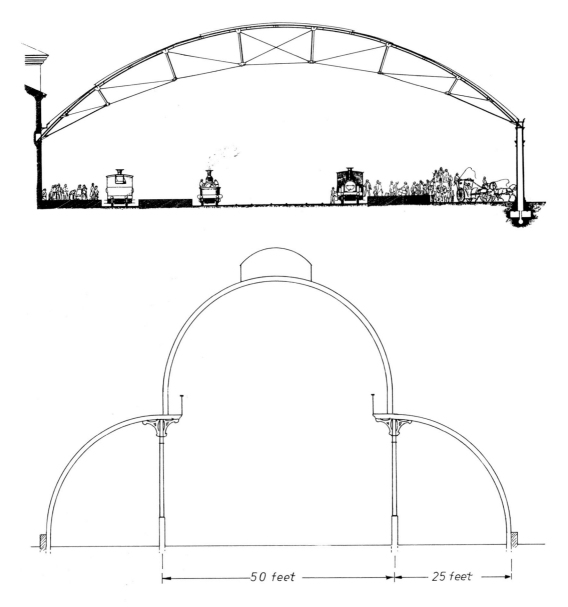

Fig. 5.6   Roofs by Richard Turner. Top: Lime Street Station from Proceedings of Institution of Civil Engineers 19 February 1850. Above: Section through the Kew Palm House - Bill Fawcett.

Since the Palm House was only taking shape in 1847 it may not have influenced Dobson significantly, but both buildings are symptoms of the age and Turner went on to design and construct the first of the really large-span arched trainsheds, for the London & North Western Railway at Lime Street Station in Liverpool. This was being rebuilt with offices designed by William Tite in collaboration with the engineer, Joseph Locke, who planned a Euston-style roof. Turner came along in the summer of 1847 and proposed a shallow arched span of 153 feet 6 inches, using deck-beam ribs only 9 inches deep, trussed by cast-iron struts and wrought-iron rods to form the earliest railway crescent-truss roof. Locke's understandable caution was satisfied by a series of tests, and the trainshed was completed in 1849[35], well before that at Newcastle although it had been conceived later. Unlike Newcastle, Lime Street enjoyed a very short life, being replaced by the first, 212 feet span of the present crescent-truss roof in 1867[36], but it was highly influential.

Both the Dobson roof and the crescent truss became popular ways of constructing a trainshed, although for large arched spans the iron lattice girder construction subsequently used by Barlow at St. Pancras provided the most robust solution. One of the earliest compliments to Dobson's roof came with the adoption of its principles by Brunel for Paddington Station, opened in 1854. Instead of Dobson's elegant arcade and its concealed wooden girder, Brunel used a deep, cross-braced girder built up from wrought-iron sections. The principals were fabricated in a similar way to Dobson's but the web was broadened out considerably towards the haunches, which spanned from top to bottom of this girder. This gave Brunel the confidence to dispense with tie rods, although this proved to be unwise and they had to be added later. The skylights at the apex of the roof used Paxton's ridge and furrow glazing, by now widely popularised through its use at his Crystal Palace, home of the Great Exhibition of 1851. The exhibition and its splendid home did much to create a climate favourable to the erection of great station sheds as symbols of prestige as well as functional objects, though the building's structure had little influence upon British station design except at Kings Cross, opened in 1852, where Lewis Cubitt followed Paxton in the use of laminated-timber arch ribs[37].

Plate 5.8 Dobson's design transformed into Paddington Station. The roof has been rebuilt much more than its Newcastle prototype: the columns are riveted plate replacements for the cast-iron originals, while the flat skylights replaced ridge-and-furrow ones running transversely. Bill Fawcett.

One of the most extensive builders of Dobson roofs was to be the North Eastern Railway (NER), where two members of the Newcastle team were to be at the heart of its station designs for many years. T. E. Harrison became Engineer-in Chief of the NER on its formation in 1854, and soon persuaded the directors to appoint a full-time architect to oversee the maintenance of their existing buildings as well as handling new work; set up in December 1854 this appears to be the earliest permanent architect's office established by any railway company anywhere in the world. Few people could have been better suited for this post than its first holder, Thomas Prosser, who had trained with his father, also an architect, then with Ignatius Bonomi before joining Dobson's office to assist with the preparation of drawings for Central Station. Prosser had then served as clerk of works on the construction of the station, and set up his own practice on its completion in 1851.

Despite this, the Dobson roof was not used on the NER's major new stations of the eighteen-sixties at Darlington Bank Top and Leeds, both since rebuilt. Darlington had a simple pitched roof while Leeds, completed in 1869, was equipped with an ungainly mansard-roofed trainshed. Though Leeds was built jointly by the NER and the London & North Western Railway, its design and construction were handled by the NER. Amends were made with the new station opened at York in 1877 and designed by Thomas Prosser, in collaboration with Harrison, shortly before Prosser's retirement due to ill-health. York's trainshed, set on a curve like Newcastle, is a tribute to Paddington but reverting to a more romantic dress, with sturdy Corinthian columns and wrought-iron arches forming the longitudinal arcades.

Plate 5.9 Repatriated from the Great Western to the North Eastern: Harrison and Prosser's trainshed at York, with the ridge-and-furrow skylights evident - though they also have now been replaced by flat panels. The signalbox, above Smith's bookstall, is a more elaborate version of the No. 2 box which stood on Newcastle's platform 8 from 1894. Bill Fawcett collection.

Following the death of one and enforced resignation of the other of Prosser's two immediate successors, William Bell took over as Chief Architect of the NER in January 1878, holding the post until his retirement at the end of 1914. Presumably with the endorsement of Harrison, who remained in office until his death in 1888, Bell reintroduced a trainshed design very close to the original Dobson roof, though with the arcades always made sturdy enough to avoid any need for concealed trusses. Bell's arched roofs appeared all over the North Eastern system, the finest being that at the new Darlington Bank Top Station, opened in 1887. There, as in the last such essay, the reconstruction of Hull Station in 1902-4, he used wrought-iron lattice girders as purlins to strengthen the structure. Bell's hand is also seen in two phases of extensions at Newcastle, including, most appropriately, the southern spans added to Dobson's trainshed in 1892-4.

Plate 5.10 Darlington Bank Top Station, showing the lattice purlins, Bell's distinctive style of skylight truss and the spandrel panels adorned with the NER's heraldic device. Bill Fawcett.

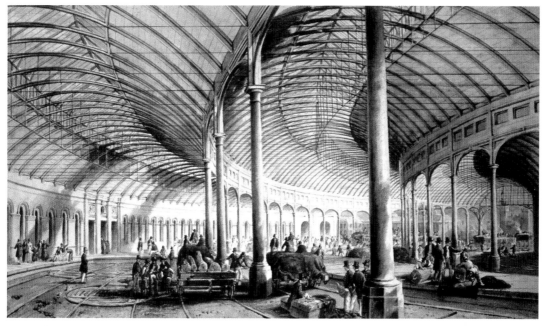

Colour Plate XI.   The interior of Central Station looking east. In the foreground on the left is one of the turntables which could be used to turn the early locomotives and carriages and transfer them between tracks. Ink and water-colour by Dobson and Carmichael.   Laing Art Gallery.

Colour Plate XII.   The interior of Central Station seen from the footbridge in 1999. The original YNB booking office, now Smith's bookshop, can be seen to the left of the main entrance. A corner of its successor, the Travel Centre, can be glimpsed on the right. Bill Fawcett.

Layout

Figure 5.7 shows the ground plan of Central Station as completed in 1851 and lacking its well-known portico. A grand entrance was nonetheless provided, modelled on Sir William Chambers' Strand vestibule to the courtyard of Somerset House - a feature drawn from the Palazzo Farnese in Rome. A central way, broad enough to accommodate carriages on the occasion of special receptions, is separated by pairs of columns from flanking footways and leads into a circulating area between the eastern and western bay platforms. The corresponding interval between the trainshed columns is made wider than the others to continue the line of the entrance across the station.

Robert Stephenson's platform layout was similar to that at another great junction station being constructed under his supervision - Chester, begun in August 1847 and completed a year later, with buildings designed by Francis Thompson and a conventional Euston-truss trainshed[38]. Both had a single long through platform with extensive bays at each end. At Newcastle the bulk of traffic would have been dealt with in the bays, since for most services the station functioned as a terminus and even the through trains on the East Coast Main Line had to reverse direction and change engines there.

From the outset the majority of trains using Central Station were local services. For example, there was a half-hourly service throughout most of the day on the North Shields line, whereas there were only four through trains each way on the Carlisle line together with one which ran as far as Haydon Bridge. Thus the initial demand on the station's resources was not great, even though the platform provision had been cut down in the course of the 1849 economies, Dobson's 1848 plan of the station (Figure 5.1) having shown an additional island platform, which would have provided one more through platform face. In 1851 therefore the southern span of the trainshed formed a carriage shed for the York Newcastle & Berwick Railway and in 1856 a glazed screen was erected across its west end down to ground level in order to provide a more hospitable environment and separate it from the tracks of the Newcastle & Carlisle outside[40].

Behind the station were engine sheds while another vanished feature of the original scene is the small square building at the north-east corner of the trainshed. On its ground floor it housed rooms used by the passenger train guards but it is likely that the parapet above this concealed a water tank for the supply of the locomotives. It was demolished to make way for the suburban concourse in the eighteen-eighties, though its walls remain below ground.

The Office Range and Portico - The Original Design

Colour Plate XIII shows Dobson's original design for the Neville Street frontage, a remarkably grandiloquent composition with two covered carriage drives meeting in an enormous porte-cochere, which also housed a central, processional carriage route on the axis of the main entrance. Externally the building would have been articulated by a giant order of paired Roman Doric columns, attached half or three-quarter columns on the flanking arcades but fully detached columns on the portico and the pavilions which acted as bookends to the arcades. Internally, the portico appears to have been designed with a flat, coffered ceiling containing one large skylight in each bay. The arcades, however, were to have transverse arches separating the bays, roofed by a stone vault with a circular skylight in the middle. This aspect of the design draws directly on Dobson's earlier Royal Arcade, and the fine effect which it would have created can be judged from the engraving of that building given in Plate 5.15.

Another conspicuous facade was required at the west end of the building to denote the head office of the Newcastle & Carlisle Railway. The company's boardroom was housed on the first floor and heralded on the outside by a line of three tall pedimented windows. On the platform frontage, the curves of the tracks and the trainshed roof were echoed in a line of arched openings, doors and windows whose positions respond to the requirements of the rooms within rather than being disposed to tie in symmetrically with the bays of the trainshed roof - nonetheless no visual disparity is ever felt since they are normally viewed in perspective.

Dobson's inspiration for the Neville Street frontage did not just spring out of thin air; indeed the covered carriage drives could well have been urged by Robert Stephenson who employed them at Chester, where they took the more modest form of spans of Euston-style roofing adjoining the arrival platform trainsheds. The use of an arcade, an Italianate feature, as a practical and impressive way of fronting a station was by 1846 becoming well established, and two earlier stations, in Cambridge and Dublin, repay attention.

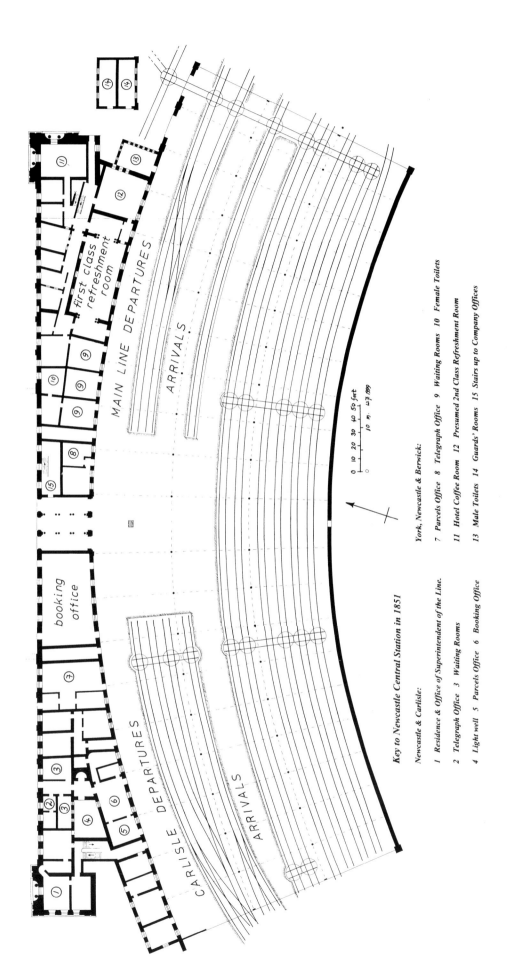

Key to Newcastle Central Station in 1851

Newcastle & Carlisle:

1 Residence & Office of Superintendent of the Line.

2 Telegraph Office 3 Waiting Rooms

4 Light well 5 Parcels Office 6 Booking Office

York, Newcastle & Berwick:

7 Parcels Office 8 Telegraph Office 9 Waiting Rooms 10 Female Toilets

11 Hotel Coffee Room 12 Presumed 2nd Class Refreshment Room

13 Male Toilets 14 Guards' Rooms 15 Stairs up to Company Offices

Fig. 5.7 Ground plan of Central Station in 1851. Bill Fawcett.

87

Colour Plate XIII. Dobson's original design for Central Station, with a portion of the hotel just visible on the left. Ink and water-colour by Dobson and Carmichael. This was Dobson's own copy of the design, reproduced by kind permission of the Natural History Society of Northumbria.

Colour Plate XIV   Dobson's revised design, with the wings and pavilion as built, but retaining the columned portico whose bold modelling would have jarred badly with the reticence of the wings. Ink and water-colour by Dobson & Carmichael. Laing Art Gallery.

Colour Plate XV. The final building, in which the awkwardness of the compromise design of Plate XIV has been resolved. The portico is the same size but the use of pilasters accords better with the severity of the flanking facades. Bill Fawcett.

Colour Plate XVI. One of Dobson's variant schemes for the portico, employing a triumphal arch, to accommodate which the columns between the arches are single instead of being paired. Laing Art Gallery.

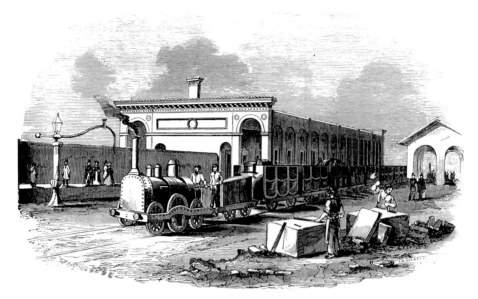

Plate 5.11 Sancton Wood's Cambridge Station seen from the tracks; the arch on the right gave access for trains. Note the lamp on top of the water crane used to supply the locomotives. Illustrated London News 1845.

Plate 5.12 Cambridge Station showing the north end of the lengthy porte-cochere. The abrupt end to the wall just left of the decorative panel shows where the trainshed was demolished, leaving just the jamb of the arch that admitted the trains. Bill Fawcett 1962.

Plate 5.13 Heuston, formerly Kingsbridge, Station in Dublin. Bill Fawcett.

Both were designed by Sancton Wood (1815-1886), an architect little known nowadays but quite successful in his own time and a former pupil of Dobson's friend and son-in-law Sydney Smirke.

Cambridge Station was opened by the Eastern Counties Railway on 29 July 1845, shortly before Hudson became involved with that company, and is a remarkable building of strongly Italianate character[42]. The front is a continuous tall arcade with fifteen semicircular arches originally forming a covered carriageway; at each end was a large arch for vehicles and a smaller one for pedestrians. Behind this were the station offices, two storeys being housed within the height of the portico, and then the entrance arcade was replicated in plainer garb as a trainshed, sheltering a single platform. Though the trainshed was removed in 1863[43] and the arcade has been encroached on by extensions to the public offices, the distinction of the original design can still be enjoyed and it is clearly the inspiration for Dobson's carriage arcades.

While Cambridge was nearing completion Wood was also working on a competition design for the Dublin terminus of the Great Southern & Western Railway, which built Ireland's second most important main line - to Cork. In September 1845 it was reported that he had won and the work was to be placed under his supervision[44]. Unlike Cambridge, the trainshed at Dublin's Heuston (formerly Kingsbridge) Station did not form part of Wood's design. Instead this was constructed under the direction of the company's Engineer-in-Chief, Sir John MacNeill, as a Euston-truss trainshed with the very heavy-looking cast-iron arcades which typify the Dublin stations. Heuston Station was completed in 1846 and outside it is an exuberant palazzo. At the head of the tracks is the block designed by Wood as a hotel but converted instead into the company's head office. Alongside what was originally the departure platform are ranged the station offices, climaxing in a booking hall fronted by an arcade much smaller in scale than that at Cambridge but dignified by Roman Doric columns in a way which seems to anticipate Dobson's treatment of the grand portico as the centrepiece of his Newcastle frontage.

Whatever the influences, they do not detract from the originality and power of Dobson's design, which would certainly have been completed had building work progressed a little faster. Whether it would have survived unmutilated, or become built up with offices and other alterations, as at Cambridge, is less clear. Dobson naturally regretted bitterly the failure to complete the building and continued to exhibit the original scheme, notably at the 1851 Exhibition and its Parisian successor in 1858.

Dobson's Revised Design

Work on the Neville Street frontage was halted in May 1849 and only restarted early in the following year[45]. During this period Dobson was obliged to make two major changes to his design. One was the deletion of the carriage arcades, the other the provision of a head office for the York Newcastle & Berwick Railway. Comparison of the ground plan published in 1848 with that of the completed building shows that no major changes were made to the other station offices and public rooms; indeed little could have been done since the carcase of these was well advanced by the time Hudson fell from office.

Under pressure from the Newcastle & Carlisle directors the revision of the frontage was carried out on the understanding that a large carriage portico would eventually be provided, though deferred for the time being. Thus the centre of the facade has been finished off as originally designed to suit the interior of the portico. The flanking wings posed more of a problem, which the architect successfully overcame to produce a work of severe nobility. Within the arcades the front wall of the station would have been similar to the present facade, with a Diocletian window[46] lighting the first floor in each bay. This wall must have reached a significant height before the changes were imposed and what Dobson has done is to frame these windows with the heavily moulded architraves originally intended for the external arches and beef up the string course on which they stand with visually supportive modillions. The crowning cornice and Doric triglyph frieze are also those originally designed for the arcades.

Colour Plate XVII   Nick Derbyshire's Travel Centre, seen shortly after completion. In the background, Smith's bookstall occupied temporary premises pending the removal of the LNER's glaring, flat-lintelled openings from the former booking office on the right and its restoration as retail premises. Bill Fawcett.

Colour Plate XVIII   Conserving the 'South Barrel Roof' as the southern Bell span is now known, in May 1999. Recladding is nearing completion and work has begun on new fully-glazed end-screens, the bottom booms for these having just been installed. The gable end of the gusset span over platforms 3 and 4 peers over the drab corrugated iron left over from the 1956 mutilations, which included removing the eastern bays of the south barrel roof where a signalbox had been cantilevered out from the rear wall. A GNER electric train stands at platform 4 and a Virgin Cross-Country HST at platform 3. Bill Fawcett.

Plate 5.14 The west pavilion of Central Station, with the River God Tyne glaring down from the keystone. Bill Fawcett c 1970.

The frontage is provided with emphatic end stops in the form of the pavilions formerly intended to terminate the arcades and now translated onto the body of the office building; these provide a splendid impression of depth and strength, with a window set well back under a coffered semi-dome. The relationship between the original design and the facade actually completed is such that much of any dressed stone already in preparation for the arcades, other than that required for the columns, could have been recycled into the present building.

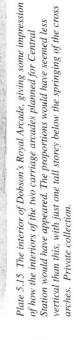

Plate 5.15 The interior of Dobson's Royal Arcade, giving some impression of how the interiors of the two carriage arcades planned for Central Station would have appeared. The proportions would have seemed less vertical than this, with just one tall storey below the springing of the cross arches. Private collection.

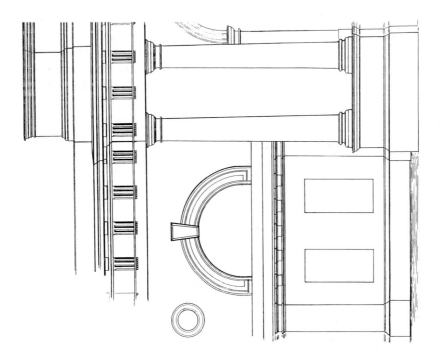

Fig. 5.8 One bay of the station facade, together with a portion of the portico. Not seen are the slit windows in those pilasters of the main, or link, facades immediately adjoining the portico. Bill Fawcett.

Dobson explored a number of schemes for the central portico, including one with an enormous central arch[47], before finishing up with a simplified version of the original design (Colour Plate XIV), which was published as a rather inaccurate sketch in the Illustrated London News shortly before the station opened[48]. For a dozen years the building languished without any portico, despite the increasing prosperity of the North Eastern Railway, but it was eventually achieved thanks to the efforts of Newcastle Town Council. In 1861 the NER and the Newcastle & Carlisle Railway decided to amalgamate. This required Parliament's consent, and so Newcastle Corporation sought a number of concessions from the NER as the price of their support for the Parliamentary Bill; one of their requirements was the construction of the portico, and the railway gave an assurance that it would be completed by the end of 1863[49].

Although the NER now had their own architect, Thomas Prosser, they had the courtesy to call on Dobson for the design, and his detailed drawings (now held in the Laing Art Gallery, Newcastle) are dated September 1861[50]. They show the portico substantially as built, except that the roof construction differs and the pedestrian entrances at each end are given rather unsuitable flat lintels instead of the arches actually executed. The work was supervised by Prosser[51], in a recreation of the original team, and Dobson had the satisfaction of seeing his masterpiece completed well before his death in December 1864. In its final form the portico has pilasters instead of the columns, which had still been intended in the revision of 1850. This economy had its contemporary critics[52] but to this writer the effect appears to be better than that which columns would have achieved; the building is more tightly-knit, and with the bold modelling of the details this conveys a tremendous impression of restrained power.

The Offices and Hotel

Though no upper-floor plan is known to survive from Dobson's original scheme, it is clear that some offices were always intended at that level. From the outset, the Newcastle & Carlisle Railway wished to move its headquarters from a temporary home in Forth House, rented from Richard Grainger, while the 1848 ground plan already shows a grand staircase leading up from the main entrance into the York Newcastle & Berwick Railway's part of the building. Hudson would have kept the main direction of the YNB at York but must have intended something more than just a few local offices to justify this ostentation - possibly a boardroom and shareholders' meeting room. After his departure the YNB sought a clean break, moved its headquarters to Newcastle and required Dobson to provide considerably increased accommodation.

Plate 5.16 YNB office gallery. Bill Fawcett 1994.

This was achieved by building administrative offices on several floors above the waiting rooms east of the main entrance and extending over that entrance and the adjoining booking hall. The cancellation of the hotel block at the east end meant that bedrooms also had to be introduced into the station building; a number were squeezed in behind the lunettes of the Neville Street frontage, each window being divided awkwardly inside to light two rooms. Nonetheless the YNB offices include two very fine interiors: double-height rooms with galleries running round at the upper level, in the manner of an early-Victorian library, to give access to continuous wall cupboards housing the company's minute books, ledgers and possibly also plans. The galleries are borne on elegantly drawn-out console brackets and reached by cast-iron spiral stairs. The Newcastle & Carlisle Railway's headquarters was at the opposite end of the building and only completed in May 1851, with a boardroom that could have doubled also as a shareholders' meeting room extending across most of the west pavilion, and spacious offices running along the first floor facing Neville Street.

Apart from the booking hall, the main public rooms of the station were concentrated east of the entrance alongside what was probably the main departure platform of the YNB, used by East Coast expresses. At the core of this area lay the first-class refreshment room, a grand interior almost 30 feet wide and 60 feet long lit by a large skylight in the middle of its deep, coved ceiling. Entry from the platform was into a vestibule and then through an opening framed by two pairs of columns; matching columns framed the bar and serving area at the far end of the room. The refreshment rooms were operated by the hotel together with its coffee room (the usual name for a hotel's main public room at that time) in the east pavilion of the Neville Street frontage. Between the refreshment rooms and the grand entrance lay the YNB waiting rooms and passenger toilets together with the telegraph office, which was used by the public as well as railway staff.

The main booking hall was the largest room in the building, and Dobson's 1848 plan shows a by-then typical layout for large stations, with a wooden office for the booking clerks projecting out from the back wall between the two doors leading onto the platform. Although the interior has been altered out of recognition, visitors to Smith's bookshop can gain a hint of the original decoration from the decorative plaster 'keystones' which adorn the eastern doorways and whose cartouches presumably once bore either the initials or heraldic device of the York Newcastle & Berwick Railway.

The station had 'closed' platforms, separated from the entrance and circulating area by cast-iron railings which also fenced off the portion occupied by the Newcastle & Carlisle Railway. This provided its own waiting rooms and booking office on a more modest scale at the west end, and, because it obstinately chose to run trains on the right-hand track rather than conform to the British norm of running them on the left, these offices were also conveniently disposed along the departure platform.

Both the offices and platforms were originally lit by gas, the latter by small glass globes bracketed out from the columns, although before its opening the trainshed had been the scene of an interesting demonstration of electricity. On the evening of 12 June 1850 W. E. Staite demonstrated to the railway directors and their friends his self-adjusting carbon-arc lamps but, although the results were said to be 'highly satisfactory', demonstrations were easy but readily-maintainable electric lighting of large public spaces was still a long way off[53].

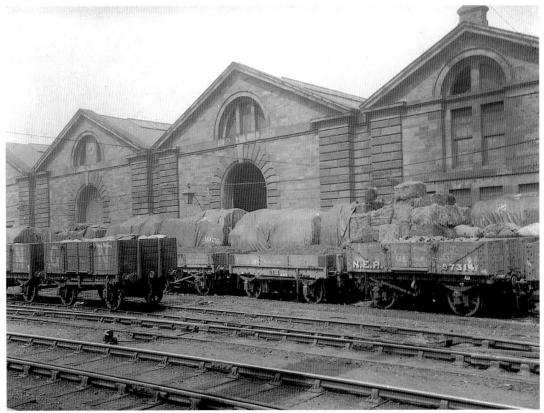

Plate 5.17 The south front of Trafalgar Goods Station, showing the prominent rustication also used by Dobson at Manors Station. Tony Cormack collection.

Allied Developments at Manors and Forth

The construction of the viaduct from Central Station to join the North Shields Railway left the original Manors Station out on a limb. Early trains on the Newcastle & Berwick line, which opened as far as Morpeth on 1 March 1847 with a daily service of three trains each way, used the old station but by the Autumn work was underway on temporary through platforms situated alongside and equipped with waiting rooms and a 'covered shed' in readiness for the opening of the temporary High Level Bridge the following year[54]. This work was supervised by Benjamin Green but the permanent station office at Manors was designed by Dobson and built in 1849. It was a small but distinctive building with round-arched openings, given a sense of presence by heavily rusticated corners and elaborate chimneys.

Nearby, the YNB built its Newcastle goods depot on land reclaimed from Pandon Dene. This once-attractive valley had become an official dumping ground for town waste and by 1849 it had been completely filled in from the railway embankment northwards as far as the 'New Bridge' of 1812, which gave its name to New Bridge Street. The railway purchased this land in October 1847[55] and on it a large goods warehouse was built, again under Dobson's supervision and using a concrete raft to cope with the unstable nature of the ground[56]. Taking its name from the adjoining street, Trafalgar Goods Station was a tall structure of one storey, intended essentially as a transhipment shed, and distinguished externally by a succession of pedimented gables with Diocletian windows. Across the line from it lay a multistorey corn warehouse, built by the YNB at the same time but designed by Benjamin Green.

All these buildings have vanished. Trafalgar Goods was demolished in 1907 to permit the construction of a link line to the former Blyth & Tyne Railway at New Bridge Street, which opened on 1 January 1909 and also obliterated Dobson's passenger station. The replacement New Bridge Street Goods Station, an early essay in reinforced concrete, was largely destroyed during the Second World War, the corn warehouse being gutted at the same time, though the ground floor of one and shell of the other survived long afterwards. The replacement Manors North passenger station was made redundant by the Metro underground route from Jesmond and subsequently demolished[57], although a mutilated Manors East station remains on the main line[58].

The completion of Central Station left the Newcastle & Carlisle Railway in possession of a large site west of Forth Banks, which had been one option for siting their passenger station. It was turned into a goods depot, and a warehouse, suspiciously similar to Dobson's at Manors though built under the supervision of the railway's engineer Peter Tate, was constructed in 1852-4[59]. This was subsequently replaced by the North Eastern Railway's large and very handsome Forth Goods Station, designed by Thomas Prosser and constructed in two phases from 1867 to 1874. At the end of the first phase, in 1871, the original N & C building was removed but re-erected and put to further use at the Central Station, where it remains. Its successor was considerably extended in 1891-2 but superseded by a new Tyneside Central Freight Depot in October 1963 and demolished down to rail level in 1972.

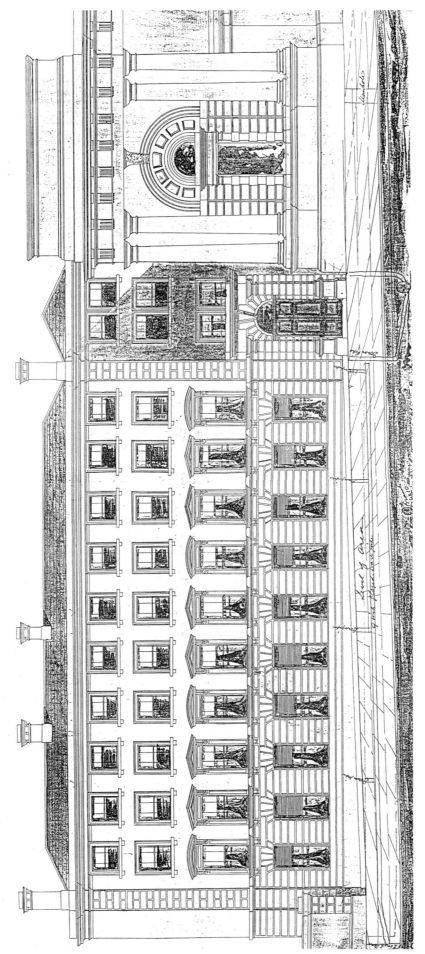

Fig. 6.1 Thomas Prosser's design for the Central Station Hotel as submitted to Newcastle Corporation in their role as a local Board of Health, hence the sewerage details. Except for the entrance in the bay linking to the station, this facade survives, framed by the much-larger extensions of 1890 onwards. Tyne & Wear Archives.

Chapter 6

The Later History of Central Station

BILL FAWCETT

Early Developments: 1851 to 1881

The first thirty years of Central Station saw a steady increase in the size and number of trains accompanied by two significant developments in the building itself: the addition of an island platform, providing two extra through platform faces, and a new hotel block.

The hotel was the last part of the station to open, with the first lease being taken by Thomas Jeffery, formerly of the Regent Hotel, Leamington, from 1 May 1852 at an initial rent of £150 p.a., rising annually to £600[1]. From the outset, hotel provision within the station building was woefully inadequate and a source of complaints from Mr. Jeffery[2]. At last, in December 1860 the North Eastern Railway agreed in principle to enlarge the hotel at an estimated cost of £6,600 in return for Jeffery paying an extra rent of £400, but nothing happened until the following September when the contract was let, Prosser doing some hasty revision of his plans during the Board meeting which considered the tenders, in order to bring the price of the successful contractors, Waite & Howard, down to £7,777-3-10[3].

The building was completed by February 1863[4] and took the form of a virtually self-contained new hotel, added to the east end of the station but still retaining the original bedrooms within the station building and servicing the refreshment rooms there. Both the location and scale of the building draw on Dobson's abandoned scheme as does the provision of a clocktower, no doubt also concealing the water tank for the hotel. Dobson's tower was a quite elaborate, Baroque affair designed to provide a strong vertical emphasis at the visually awkward junction between his grand arcade and a rather commonplace hotel facade. Prosser's hotel elevation is somewhat better, although it may well draw on discussions with Dobson, who had had plenty of time to rethink his ideas. As executed, the building was four stories high, with a prominently rusticated ground floor and corners; the link to the station housed the hotel entrance but was discreetly recessed on the upper floors. Though later hugely extended, both sideways and upwards, Prosser's facade is still on show. (Colour Plate X)

The merger with the Newcastle & Carlisle Railway, which had been under consideration since the closing months of 1858[5], took effect in 1862 and brought the working of Central Station under a single management and the running of Carlisle trains on to the left-hand track. One of the early improvements made was to the platform height. Originally these were only 15 inches above rail level[6], quite a generous height in 1850, but, after conducting tests at York Station, the NER decided to adopt a platform height of 2 feet 8 inches at its larger stations, not far short of the eventual Board of Trade recommendation of 3 feet. This was achieved at Newcastle during 1866[7] by lowering the tracks, the resulting descent into the station proving a minor factor in a subsequent incident when a train drove into the buffers of one of the east-end bays[8]. As well as providing higher platforms some remodelling took place, including the provision of an extra bay platform on the north side at the east end, probably for local departures to Tynemouth.

Several new lines opened during the eighteen-sixties which put more pressure on the station. One was a branch from the Carlisle line, near Blaydon, up the Derwent Valley to Consett, which opened to passengers on 2 December 1867, followed on 1 December 1868 by the new main line route along the Team Valley from Durham. To cope with all this an island platform was brought into use, apparently in 1871, increasing the number of through platforms from one to three but swallowing up the space formerly used for storing carriages in the southern span of the trainshed[9]. Fortunately the old Forth Goods Station was now redundant and needing to be removed from the path of its successor. So this substantial stone building was taken down and re-erected, two roof bays longer, at the west end of the Central Station site, alongside the then alignment of Forth Banks[10]. Six carriage sidings ran through the building and access was provided by a traverser which bore carriages sideways to and from a further 6 tracks located outside and linked with the running lines. Although long-blocked, the broad archway for the traverser can still be seen in the east wall of the building, indicating just how short railway carriages were at that time.

Plate 6.1 An early photograph, taken soon after the completion of the portico in 1863. The original ribbed cladding of the trainshed roof, later replaced by slates, is clearly visible. Glimpsed behind the hotel is a corner of the block of guards' rooms, which may have formed a water tower and whose style is echoed in Prosser's gate lodge on the left. Showing up above the hotel is the clocktower, a far cry from Dobson's Baroque flourish but still remaining though now even less visible. The lamp on the right conceals John Lough's statue of George Stephenson, erected in 1862 as part of this creation of a grand urban space. Unfortunately two grossly bad buildings of the late nineteen-sixties now do their best to ruin the scene. Newcastle City Libraries.

Plate 6.2 The portico clocks were added when the clocktower became hidden behind the hotel extensions. Curiously, the keystones of the carriage arches remain 'in block', without the carving originally intended. Bill Fawcett.

Plate 6.3 The main entrance about 1970. Bill Fawcett.

The building and fitting out of the carriage shed was virtually complete by June 1873[11] but it lasted only ten years in this condition before offices were built on top for that section of the Accountant's staff engaged in auditing used tickets. The original roof columns seem to have been retained but iron beams were carried across from them to the outside walls to support a single office floor. The walls were raised and the building re-roofed in three spans running along its length, instead of the former nine transverse spans. The roof was well endowed with skylights, and a line of offices occupied each outer span while the middle one provided a light well for the carriage shed below. At the Neville Street end the NER Architect, William Bell, designed an imposing entrance block in which offices for the Revenue Accountant and his senior clerks flanked a spacious foyer whose Francophile lantern roof covers twin stairs which rise the short distance from street to office level with surprising grandeur. (Colour Plate IX)

Plate 6.4 No. 1 Neville Street. The Revenue Accountant had his office in the right-hand side, beyond which is seen the earlier carriage shed. Bill Fawcett.

The role of the administrative offices at Newcastle began to change with the formation in 1854 of the NER. The General Manager of the merged companies was based at York, together with the Chief Accountant, but the Engineer-in-Chief, Harrison, continued to have his office in Central Station and Board meetings were held in both places, transferring in 1863 from the eastern offices into the Carlisle boardroom at the west end[12]. From the eighteen-seventies onwards there was an increasing concentration of the NER bureaucracy in York, culminating in the opening of a splendid new headquarters there in 1906, but Newcastle remained an important alternative venue for directors' meetings.

Transformation: 1882 to 1894

In 1882, Newcastle, which had been a county in its own right since 1400 and was now the capital of one of the world's most innovative industrial regions, at last received its charter as a city. As if to celebrate, the NER took the first steps in an expansion scheme which would take until 1894 to complete but equipped Central Station to cope with little further change in its basic layout until the nineteen-seventies. The result is shown in Fig. 6.2.

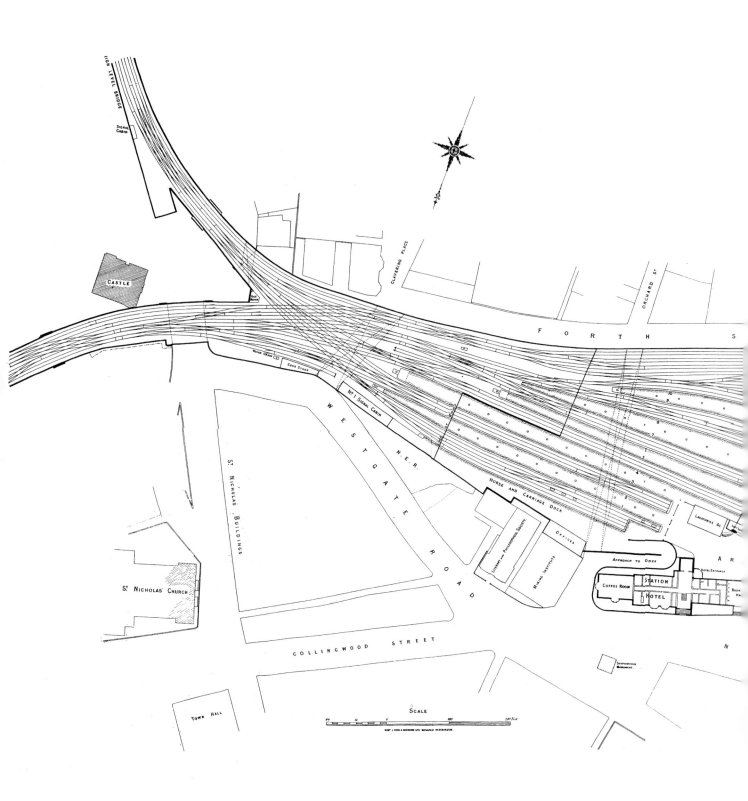

HIGH LEVEL BRIDGE

SIGNAL CABIN

CASTLE

Coal House

CLAVERING PLACE

ORCHARD ST

FORTH S

WATER CRANE

COKE STAGE

No 1 SIGNAL CABIN

N.E.R.

WESTGATE ROAD

St NICHOLAS BUILDINGS

St NICHOLAS CHURCH

LITERARY AND PHILOSOPHICAL SOCIETY

MINING INSTITUTE

HORSE AND CARRIAGE DOCK

OFFICES

APPROACH TO DOCK

LAVATORIES &c

10
9
8
7
6
5
4
3
2
1

A R

STATION HOTEL

HOTEL ENTRANCE

COFFEE ROOM

OFFICE

BOOK HALL

N

COLLINGWOOD STREET

STEPHENSON MONUMENT.

TOWN HALL

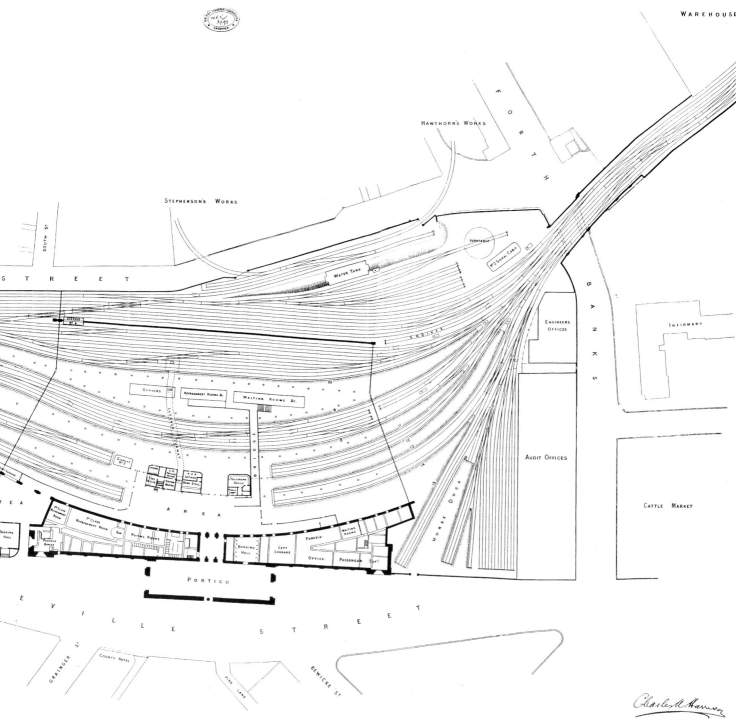

Fig. 6.2   NER plan of Central Station in 1893. Note the two lines heading across Forth Street to convey materials into the
locomotive works of Robert Stephenson & Co. and R & W Hawthorn.   Public Records Office.

Plate 6.5 The hotel (not yet 'Royal') depicted in an NER carriage print. This shows the first extension overpowering Prosser's original block on the right. This later had more floors added on top, evening up the appearance of the building. Bill Fawcett collection.

By the eighteen-eighties it was apparent that the station could not continue to cope with the increasing length and frequency of trains, particularly given developments in suburban services on Tyneside. In 1874 the NER had taken over the last significant independent railway in Northumberland, the Blyth & Tyne, and acquired a second route from Newcastle to Tynemouth, via Whitley. It now set out to integrate this into a coherent suburban network by constructing a new line along the coast to link with the original route to Tynemouth via North Shields. This link, the present Metro route through Cullercoats, opened in July 1882 and the obvious counterpart was a line within Newcastle to divert trains from the old Blyth & Tyne terminus at New Bridge Street into Central. Unfortunately, this was not to be achieved until 1909[13] but the capacity to handle all suburban traffic at Central Station was provided well before this by the construction of what was almost a separate station, with its own dedicated platforms, concourse and booking office.

Originally, the NER seem to have planned an enlargement of the station at the east end only, in order to accommodate new suburban platforms on the north side, together with lengthening the existing platforms[14]. This would have left the through platforms and main concourse quite cramped, and so an extension was also planned to the south, involving a diversion of Forth Street onto the alignment it now occupies. The necessary land purchases were enabled by the NER Acts of 1883 and 1889 and greatly simplified by the pattern of land ownership and the co-operative attitude of Newcastle Corporation, which regarded the work as a civic improvement. Indeed, of the property affected near the foot of Westgate Road, one councillor remarked that 'if nothing more was done than the removal of that rookery of immorality and the large number of thieves and vagabonds who live in the neighbourhood . . it would be a great advantage'[15]. This was no mere rhetoric - the old houses in the area had become crowded tenements for the poor and in December 1889, after site clearance had been completed, Newcastle's Medical Officer of Health reported that 103 houses with a population of 1,024 people had been closed as a result of the railway's activities and the extensions being carried out nearby to the Head Post Office in St. Nicholas' Square[16].

At this time the NER was also engaged on an expensive new station and lines at Darlington, and seems to have been in no mood to hurry with the Newcastle enlargement, though negotiations with the Virgin Mary Hospital, which owned much of the land needed, began in September 1884[17]. The Corporation took the opportunity to improve access between the city centre and the forgotten backlands of Forth Street and Clavering Place by negotiating improved link roads below the extended station, notably Orchard Street, and all this, together with land transfers between the company and council, was settled by the beginning of 1889. Meanwhile there had been an intriguing temporary extension to handle traffic to the Royal Agricultural Society Show at Newcastle in July 1887. This was an additional through platform behind the station: a timber structure with access only from Forth Street over which it encroached for some feet[18, 19].

The first contracts for the station extensions were let on 20 September 1888 and comprised the substructure to carry the platforms and tracks, together with an enormous enlargement of the hotel[20]. This was badly needed; the company was engaged in a programme of improving its hotels and taking over their management, Newcastle being taken in hand in May 1887, on the expiry of the tenant's lease. The Station Hotel was the second most profitable on the system, raising £4,827 in 1888, but this was well below its full potential. York's Royal Station Hotel made £8,643 in the same year, but that was a spacious new building[21].

Rebuilding was not yet an option, so William Bell, the NER architect, extended the Newcastle hotel to the east, two storeys higher and with modest hints of the fashionable French Second Empire style. His facade is somewhat banal, but the glory of the building remains in Bell's extensive use of Burmantoft's faience throughout the interiors of the public rooms. This architectural tilework, supplied by the Leeds Fireclay Company - one of the leading manufacturers, provided a durable, washable surface whose considerable expense was offset by the saving in painting bills. It also offered some handsome glowing colours, notably a rich brown. The hotel interiors, using a fashionable English Renaissance style, were extensively reported in the *British Architect*[22] and the directors were persuaded to adopt a similar treatment for the refurbishment of Dobson's first-class refreshment room in 1893, setting up a committee to settle the details of style and colour with the architect[23]. Significantly, the leading member was the company's deputy chairman, Joseph Whitwell Pease, a friend and client of the architect Alfred Waterhouse, perhaps the most notable exponent of terracotta exteriors and faience interiors.

Plate 6.6 Burmantoft's faience on display in the hotel foyer. The door ahead led on to the suburban concourse. The reception kiosk looks rather like a fantasy of a booking office. 'British Architect' 10 November 1893.

The Entrance Hall
shewing
The Station Entrance.

By February 1891 construction of the arches to carry the extension must have been nearing completion, since contracts were being let in connection with the building of the new platforms[24]. Finally, on 21 January 1892 a contract for the extensions to the trainshed was let to the Tees Side Iron & Engine Works (later well-known as the Tees Bridge & Engineering Company), successors to the unfortunate Hopkins Gilkes who had built the first and fallen Tay Bridge[25]. At the same time work was underway on the widening of the line to Manors, whose completion in June 1894 brought the new station platforms into full use[26].

Central Station in 1894
The most impressive and lasting feature of the enlargement was the southerly extension of the trainshed in an updated version of Dobson's design to shelter a new island platform and a number of sidings. Like the trainshed recently completed at Darlington (1887) it dispensed with intermediate ribs between the supporting columns and used purlins to strengthen the structure instead, although the I-section wrought-iron purlins at Newcastle have a heavy appearance compared with the lattice girders employed at Darlington Bank Top. A distinctive Bell detail is the treatment of the large skylight and roof vent with its O-ring frame and rounded cap. Among various hints at economy is the use of a standard design of cast-iron spandrel panel in the arcade at the junction of the Dobson and Bell roofs. This provides two intermediate console brackets, useful on one side where they carry the intermediate ribs of the Dobson roof but looking rather silly on the other where they are superfluous. Waiting and refreshment rooms were provided on the new platform in a building carefully designed to harmonise with Dobson's work, while it was linked to the rest of the station by a spacious and gently ramped footbridge, together with an underground subway and lifts for parcels and postal traffic.

The tracks on the north side of the 1871 island platform were blocked in the middle to form two pairs of bays and provide an enlarged circulating area, so the remodelled station still had only three through platforms but they and the bays extended much further to the east than before.

Plate 6.7 The replacement end-screens, installed 1892-3, are seen behind a visitor from the North British Railway, which enjoyed running powers over the NER from Border Counties Junction, just west of Hexham. NB locomotives originally used the former N&C engine shed in the angle of Forth Street and Forth Banks, swept away during the 1890s extensions. This photograph was taken before the alterations made in connection with the opening of the King Edward Bridge in 1906. Tony Cormack collection.

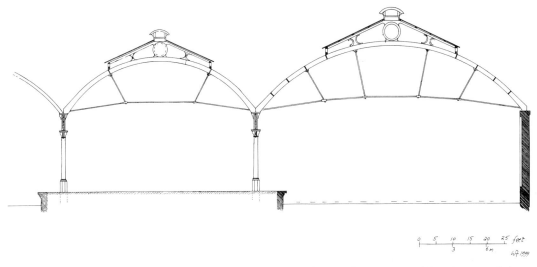

Fig. 6.3   Transverse section through the two spans designed by William Bell as a southern extension of the Dobson trainshed. Section taken about half-way along the platform. The office range on the island platform has been omitted for clarity. Bill Fawcett.

Plate 6.8 The Bell spans under construction. Lying on the platform are frames for Bell's distinctive skylights - quite different from those of the original roof. On the ground at the right is a portion of a rib, revealing the use of rivetted fishplates to join segments. A glimpse is caught of the Dobson roof on its new arcade, replacing the former rear wall, but vistas between the old and new trainsheds are blocked by the new office range. Newcastle City Libraries.

Plate 6.9 A favourite vantage point for photographers: Wilson Worsdell's Class S1 No. 2113 at the east end of platform 8. It was completed at Gateshead Works in June 1901 and, to judge from the mix of gas and electric lighting, photographed soon after. The ridge and furrow roofing added to the east end of the station extended for 9 bays across the main-line platforms (8, 9 & 10) as well as the terminal platforms, which had a further 5 bays sheltering them only. Note the platform signs with hands pointing towards the tracks. Tony Cormack collection.

Plate 6.10 The roof was borne on deep, wrought-iron lattice girders running along the ridges and extending to a glazed screen perched above Forth Street. Outlined against this is 'Tennant' Class No. 1474, built at Gateshead in 1885. It stands on the station sidings, while the tracks beyond led behind the rear wall of the trainshed and were used as avoiding lines by goods and excursion trains. J.M. Fleming collection.

Plate 6.11 Roof construction revealed by the demolition of the span from platform 8 to Forth Street during the early years of British Railways. Photographed c1970. Bill Fawcett.

The hotel entrance was transferred into the new wing and its former entrance was rebuilt to provide access into a suburban concourse formed between the outer wall of the original trainshed and the back of the hotel, part of whose ground floor was also transformed into a suburban booking office with its own street access. East of this concourse four bay platforms were provided, although one of these, alongside the hotel, was taken as a horse and carriage loading dock. The east end concourse, sometimes known as Tynemouth Square, was covered with a fully-glazed ridge and furrow roof giving it a very light appearance. The local platforms were covered with a high ridge and furrow roof carried on deep lattice girders and partially extending across the east end of the main-line platforms to a glazed screen wall perched on the Forth Street retaining wall of the station site. Though totally different from the Dobson spans, this new roof, again fully glazed, was effective and attractive. The end screens of the Dobson roof were incompatible with the extensions and were replaced.

Plate 6.12 A corner of the suburban concourse, with the hairdressing saloon which was once an essential feature of any major station. Photographed 1977. John Mallon.

Central Station now had 15 platforms, whose use was described by E. M. Bywell in the *Railway Magazine* for January 1901. Numbers 1, 2 and 3 were the new suburban platforms used principally by trains to and from Tynemouth, while the remaining east end bays, numbers 4 to 7, were chiefly used for trains to South Shields and Sunderland and local services on the main line. Platform 8 was the largest of the through platforms, 1,135 feet long and up to 40 feet wide, and, according to Bywell, used in preference to the island platforms 9 and 10 (themselves a thousand feet long) for East Coast expresses.

At the west end, bay platforms 11 to 14 were used for trains to Carlisle and Consett while number 15, which lay outside the station roof almost on the site of the original Newcastle & Carlisle Railway Forth terminus, was not regularly used by passengers. Since this platform numbering remained in use for almost a century it will be adopted in the subsequent description of developments up to the introduction of main-line electrification.

Bywell pointed out that the station handled a daily average of 700 trains, with occasional peaks up to a thousand, and it was for many years regarded as the busiest British station outside London, although this must be qualified by noting that Newcastle was unusual and fortunate among British cities in having a single main station, rather than several serving competing companies. To run this business Mr. Holliday, the stationmaster, had 11 assistant stationmasters (distributed between shifts, of course); 96 signalmen; 300 porters, ticket-collectors and miscellaneous others; 20 shunters; 170 guards; 16 clerks and a further 22 booking clerks, who issued over three million tickets in 1899; while the parcels department employed another 34 clerks whose 1899 workload included 8,469 horses, 8,969 dogs and 93,376 cans of milk, the milk platform being at the west end[27].

1894 to 1922: Electrification and a New Bridge.

At the start of the twentieth century, Tyneside was home to some of the pioneering ventures in public electricity supply and these were to have both good and bad effects on the railway. The new extension to the station hotel was lit by electricity from the outset and in 1900 the NER embarked on replacing the gas lighting on the platforms by electric arc-lamps, just fifty years after Mr. Staite's promising demonstration[28].

Plate 6.13 NER Brochure. Bill Fawcett collection.

A less welcome electrification was that of the municipal tramways, a thorn in the flesh of railway companies who often felt that their competition for suburban traffic was being subsidised out of the local rates to which the railways were heavy contributors. The Newcastle tramways had begun in 1879 and remained horse-drawn until 1901 when the Corporation introduced electric traction[29]. Electric trams, reaching conveniently close to home and work, had a severe impact on the short suburban journeys which made up a large part of the NER's passenger business on Tyneside but this had been foreseen by the company's energetic General Manager, George Stegmann Gibb, who persuaded his directors to embark on the electrification of their coast route running from Central Station to Tynemouth and Whitley Bay and returning to New Bridge Street. Their consultant was Charles Hesterman Merz, of Newcastle, who had already overseen the electrification of the Cork tramways and became the leading figure in the development of the electricity supply network in Britain. Unlike other railways, the NER did not build their own generating station but at Merz's urging agreed to use the public supply, thereby encouraging its growth - to the benefit of all.

The line was electrified at 600 Volts d.c. on a third-rail system, and services began between New Bridge Street and Benton on 29 March 1904, extended in stages to Monkseaton, Tynemouth and Central Station, where electric running appeared from 1 July 1904[30].

The electric trains were an immediate success, offering much better acceleration than their steam-hauled predecessors, and reversed the trend in passenger bookings. In the area served these had been almost ten million in 1901 but fallen to a low of just under six million in 1903; by 1905 they were nearing seven and reached over ten million before the First World War intervened[31]. Just as important was a considerable reduction in running costs, compared with steam operation, and this led to thoughts of electrifying the line along the south bank of the Tyne to South Shields, and an even more ambitious idea - the electrification of the main line from Newcastle to York, which was NER policy in 1920 but had to wait seventy years to be implemented.

The royal opening of the King Edward Bridge in 1906 was marked by inserting a relief of the King's head over the main entrance to Central Station, between those of his parents. The new bridge enabled Anglo-Scottish trains to run through the station without reversing, though for many years they continued to change engines there. Changes to the west end of Central Station included realigning the bays, extending platforms on quite a sharp curve and providing them with glazed verandah roofs outside the trainshed[32]. A particularly fine glass roof was put over platforms 14, 15 and the loading docks, using slender trussed-beams which gave a more elegant appearance than the east-end roofing. Fronted on Neville Street by a handsome screen wall with lunettes echoing those of the original station, the new roof also copied Dobson in the design of its columns. To make space for all this the carriage shed, which had already fallen out of use and become a storage area, was trimmed back along a gently curving line.

Plate 6.14 Pilot engines were used to shunt stock around the station. Behind No. 68736 is the curving wall of the Revenue Accountant's Office and former carriage shed, with part of the 1906 platform roofing to the right. Though much shortened in 1906, the building in the foreground continued to present a bold neo-classical pediment to the outside world until its demolition during the later years of British Rail. The station pilot is seen in the special livery it received in 1960: green with both the NER heraldic device and British Railways' armorial emblem. This class of locomotive, Wilson Worsdell's E1, is notable for the longevity of its design - the first having been built in 1898 and the last in 1951. Ian S. Carr.

The parcels department, which had operated at the west end of the station, was moved out of the way to premises alongside the former carriage dock at the east end, opposite platform 1, the considerable fish traffic into the city also being transferred nearby. Some use was made of the arches below the station, but the new parcels office of 1906 was displayed to the outside world, namely Westgate Road, in the rather incongruous form of a tall wooden frontage of entirely functional aspect, finishing in three gables. Some amends for this curiosity were provided in 1910 by the construction of Irving House, a short distance along the same street, named after George Irving the NER's Estate Agent from 1855 to 1906, and still proudly bearing the company's initials on its very-respectable facade.

Plate 6.15 The Parcels Office frontage on to Westgate Road. The upswept wall to the right of the bridge formed the rear wall of No. 1 signalbox from 1893 to 1909. The screened-in arch below it housed the early road motor vehicles of the parcels department. Photographed 1977. John Mallon.

This was the last significant development carried out at Central Station by the North Eastern Railway. During World War I the railways operated under government control and afterwards Parliament determined on their rationalisation by enforcing a merger into just four new companies. The 'Grouping', as it was called, saw the NER become the largest partner in a new London & North Eastern Railway (LNER), with effect from 1 January 1923.

Life with the LNER: 1923 to 1947
The LNER was created just after the collapse of a brief post-war boom, and spent most of the years up to the Second World War struggling against economic adversity in the Depression which had so particularly severe an impact on Tyneside. Little capital investment was therefore seen or needed on the local railways, although one scheme which did get through was the long-contemplated electrification of the line to South Shields, with services starting on 14 March 1938.

Despite its difficulties, the LNER was conscientious about maintaining its assets in good order and these included the station hotel. The extensions of 1888-90 had been followed by building further floors on top of Prosser's original building but there remained a need for more bedrooms and function rooms. In 1913 the NER briefly considered total rebuilding but this was too costly and the last major extension was made in 1923 - a new wing sprouting out from the rear of the building and bridging across the vehicle ramp to provide bedrooms and a banqueting room[33]. Twelve years later, the construction of a new lounge involved some encroachment onto the suburban concourse and the creation of the present modestly Art-Deco entrance from the station, possibly to the design of W.J. Smith of the much scaled-down LNER architect's office at York[34].

Plate 6.16 The most potent image of the LNER is provided by Sir Nigel Gresley's handsome Pacifics, which hauled East Coast expresses for 4 decades until the nineteen-sixties. A3 No. 60065 'Knight of the Thistle' was slipping violently as it left for Kings Cross with the 'Heart of Midlothian' express in a gale on 13 April 1960. The curved ribs are still evident in the skylights of the Dobson roof, but the end-screens seem not to have been restored after the glass was stripped in World War II, nor was the glass replaced in the verandah roofs on these platforms. Ian S. Carr.

   Early photographs of Central Station show a vast expanse of clear platforms, but by the early nineteen-hundreds this had all changed. Passengers walking through the grand entrance were faced with a jolly colony of wooden buildings flanking the footbridge and the entrance to platform 8, against which they provided an effective barrier. This had begun with the building of the first 'station signalbox', followed by the telegraph office, and proved a useful way not only of housing the overflow of passenger facilities from Dobson's buildings but of providing a shop window for those businesses which might need it, such as Smith's bookstall and the Continental Enquiry Office, later leased to the Fred Olsen shipping line. The LNER should have heeded this when embarking on their reorganisation of the main booking office in 1936. The idea was sensible: concentrate the booking and enquiry functions in opposite sides of the same office; the booking screens were attractive period pieces but the enormous horizontal windows and gaping entrances slammed into Dobson's facades were a thoughtless mutilation. Fortunately, after fifty years British Rail undid the damage and restored the original design.

Plate 6.17 The main concourse decorated for the coronation of Queen Elizabeth in 1953, showing the wooden buildings which divided it from platform 8. Ken Hoole collection.

Plate 6.18 Looking east along platform 8 from the footbridge past the backs of the bookstall and stationmaster's office, demolished in November 1984 to make way for the present Travel Centre. Beyond them is No. 2 signalbox. Note the signals bracketed out from the roof columns and bearing the distinctive 'mushroom and spike' finials of McKenzie & Holland, the NER's contractors. This photograph was probably taken soon after the introduction of electric lighting in 1901. Newcastle City Libraries.

Plate 6.19 No. 2 signalbox, opened in June 1894 and closed in April 1959. The building subsequently caught fire but damage to the station roof was confined to the bays above. This splay-cornered design gave good visibility of parcels trolleys and other hazards on the busy platforms, and a similar box survives at York Station, though long since put to other use. Hugh Murray collection.

Plate 6.20 The telegraph office began life near the station entrance. The ground floor of this wooden building on platform 8, with its bold cornice and slender corner pilasters, was probably built about 1880 to cope with the expansion of the office and free up the original site for more passenger toilets. The first floor was added in 1911, accommodation also being provided for the assistant stationmasters and the station's telephone switchboard. Later, as the telegraph function shrank, the locomotive inspectors, station inspectors and letter sorting office moved into the redundant areas. Photographed 1977. John Mallon.

Central Station escaped damage during the Second World War though the glass had to be removed temporarily from the trainshed roofs as an air-raid precaution. Afterwards the LNER examined a number of improvement schemes throughout the system and at Newcastle they considered the provision of extra through platforms. Scope for further expansion to the south had been made by the NER's purchase of land beyond Forth Street[35] but the LNER was looking at less expensive options. Drawings made in July 1947[36] show the bay platforms, 6 & 7 and 10 & 11 joined up to provide two through lines, and a narrow platform, only 535 feet long, squeezed in against the rear wall of the trainshed. The footbridge was to be replaced by a subway. The idea came to nothing; although an easy way to get more through platforms, it would have constricted the circulating area very badly, nonetheless the thought of linking up the bays continued to find support.

Hope and Despair: 1948 to 1970

On 1 January 1948 Britain's railways were taken into public ownership. This was intended to benefit both users and staff but, while it brought some public investment into a network worn out by its war effort, this was not accompanied by a realistic rethinking of the railway's role at the top of the British Railways Board. The LNER had been a pioneer in abandoning hopelessly unprofitable rural passenger services, and the North Eastern Region of British Railways showed equal realism, giving up routes such as those to Consett (the Derwent Valley route closed to passengers in May 1955), where they could not compete with a frequent bus service, and replacing steam traction on local services with diesel multiple units, which succeeded in attracting passengers.

During the nineteen-fifties Central saw little structural change, other than the cutting back of the east-end high-level roof across the main-line platforms 8 to 10, and its replacement in 1956 by low cantilevered steel platform awnings of a functional but wholly inappropriate design. Also underway at this time was a total resignalling, with colour-light signals replacing the huge gantries of semaphores and a large new signalbox being built on a girder bridge spanning platform 10 and the adjoining tracks; this was commissioned in 1959. Surprisingly, perhaps, the nineteen-fifties brought a pressing need for further administrative offices within the station, for the staff of the Area Traffic Manager. This was solved in a very ingenious and unobtrusive way by taking out the roof of the portico and replacing it with a single floor of offices, lit by rooflights and carried on 3 feet deep girders; the work was carried out during 1959-60[37].

Plate 6.21 Hawker Siddeley's experimental locomotive 'Kestrel' standing in platform 8 in the same position as the engine in Plate 6.9. Below the truncated east-end roofing, the replacement cantilevered awning is stepped up to clear the water crane provided for steam locomotives. Photographed 29 October 1969. Ian S. Carr

During the early nineteen-sixties an economist, Richard Beeching (1913-85), was brought in, first to analyse the problems of an increasingly debt-ridden railway and then to run it. Some of his conclusions conveyed a necessary realism, others were totally bizarre - such as the suggestion of withdrawing express services from the East Coast Main Line north of Newcastle and diverting them on to the West Coast via the Newcastle & Carlisle line[38]. One of his best efforts, which typifies the institutionalised vandalism of the period, was the remark that he would like to rebuild every station on the system. Central Station was not immune from such contempt and schemes were floated first to destroy everything but the portico and then to get rid of that as well. These were not well received locally, and fortunately British Rail, as it had smartly become, was too busy making a mess of stations in cities like Birmingham instead.

Meanwhile steam locomotives were vanishing from Britain's railways and became extinct, for normal B.R. services, in 1967, a year which also saw the merger of British Rail's North Eastern Region into its Eastern Region, and the abandonment of electric traction on Tyneside - replaced by diesel trains with a hopelessly inadequate acceleration.

Plate 6.22 The last electric services on the North Tyne circle ran on 17 June 1967. Thirty years earlier the LNER had introduced Gresley's articulated stock, seen here in platform 3 forming the 13.03 express to Tynemouth via Jesmond, which ran non-stop between Manors and West Monkseaton. On the extreme right is the parcels platform. British Railways introduced new standards of lighting to Central Station, ingeniously employing conical clusters of fluorecent tubes within the trainshed. Outside were these slim concrete standards, with 'Newcastle' printed on the lamp cover. Ian S. Carr.

Plate 6.23 The west-end roofing is lower than the earlier work at the east end, and employs a lighter version of the same structural system. The wooden building was constructed in 1906 as waiting rooms, part of an enhancement of west-end passenger facilities in connection with platform rearrangement, but was soon given over to other uses. The dining car kitchens were serviced from premises to the left of this building, a site now partly occupied by the 'Red Star' parcels office. Bill Fawcett.

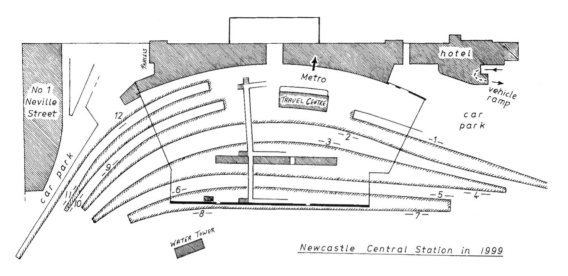

Fig. 6.4 Central Station in 1999

Renewal: 1971 to 1999

The nineteen-seventies brought a new hope and vigour to Britain's railways. On Tyneside, the formerly electrified suburban routes were drawn into an imaginative new electric light railway network, the Metro, promoted by a Tyneside Passenger Transport Authority, created in 1969. Under an Act of 1973 and over a time span of almost eleven years, new lines were built, largely underground, from Jesmond to Gateshead and St. James to Heaton. The Metro, now penetrating right through the city centre, integrated with feeder bus services and later extended to Newcastle Airport, was a great success. Central Station naturally lost all its services to the coast, and the suburban station (platforms 1 and 2) closed following the opening of the first phase of the Metro, between Haymarket and Tynemouth, on 11 August 1980. Platforms 1 to 3 and the parcels dock had their tracks finally disconnected on 13 March 1983 and removed during the following months. The east end roofing had gradually been cut back to a fringe over the parcels dock and this was now removed, leaving only the roof over the old suburban concourse. The parcels traffic was concentrated at the west end of the station, and the abandoned east end bays were filled in and given over to much-needed car parking for railway and hotel users, which was later extended over the site of bays 4 and 5 as well.

The development of a shoppers' paradise, the 'Metro Centre', on waste land west of Gateshead led, after some delay, to the opening of a new station on the Carlisle line, which had been diverted in October 1982 from its original route through Scotswood on to what had been predominantly a freight line on the south bank of the Tyne. This led to services running through from the Sunderland line, some terminating at the Metro Centre, others continuing further west, but this showed up the inadequacies of Central Station. Having lost most of its suburban traffic to the Metro, here was a large station, still lavishly endowed with under-used bays but with only three through platforms. The solution lay in the avoiding lines behind the station, formerly used by goods trains and excursions. The decline in freight traffic and abandonment of the original Carlisle route to Blaydon except for a half-mile long stump serving the civil engineer's Forth Yard and a cement terminal meant that the avoiding lines were now little needed.

The key to financing new platforms was East Coast electrification, which in any case entailed a remodelling of the track layout and new signalling. Work began with the construction of a new island platform straddling the rear wall of the trainshed. By the Autumn of 1989 the footbridge had been extended through to the new island, one face of which was already in use while arches were being made through the wall to its other side. Meanwhile Platform 10 (in the 1894 numbering) was out of use while its alignment was straightened - being built out to remove the curve at the east end. Electric traction was introduced in stages, and on Wednesday 12 June 1991 the Tees-Tyne Pullman became the first passenger train to run from Newcastle to Kings Cross hauled throughout by an electric locomotive.

Central Station now has one east end bay - No. 1 (formerly platform 7), together with four more versatile ones at the west end - Nos. 9-12 (formerly 11-14). Through platforms 2-4 (formerly 8-10) are generally used by the express services of Virgin and Great North Eastern Railway, while the faces of the new island are divided to provide platforms 5-8 normally used by Northern Spirit trains. The stump of the old Carlisle line has acquired a role as a holding area for empty stock, notably the very-successful 'High Speed Trains' which monopolised East Coast services prior to electrification and are still a major feature.

The re-ordering of platforms had been preceded by a rethinking of passenger facilities. Closure of the suburban station encouraged a focus on the circulating area around the main entrance, resulting in the transfer of the booking and enquiry offices into a new building on the site of the wooden structures which used to greet the traveller. The design of a quite large building, freestanding within the Dobson trainshed, posed a problem. It could easily have been done as a pastiche of the original office range but this would have been visually intrusive. Instead, the architect, Nick Derbyshire, sought to introduce a modern, 'high-tech' design, highly visible but with a transparency which responds to the technology of the trainshed itself. Thus the bulk of the centre is clad with a dark, reflective glass but the front is a lighter verandah structure, allowing one to see through to Dobson's roof columns as well as highlighting its own structure; on top is a railway carrying the window-cleaning equipment. Completed in 1985, this established a style which was then taken up in the design of the cantilevered roof over the new platform (7 & 8) at the rear of the station.

In the nineteen-sixties, the station concourse still possessed a restaurant and tearoom, quite apart from Dobson's first-class refreshment room, which had become the general buffet. By the eighties only the buffet remained, together with a refreshment room on what were then platforms 9 and 10, and its faience interior had been painted over in a misguided attempt to modernise its image. Fortunately, before any further damage could be done, a new refreshment room was formed inside the offices next to the station entrance, while the vacated booking hall and office on the opposite side were converted for letting as retail units and had door and window openings reinstated to the original pattern. During this time No. 1, Neville Street, the former Accountant's Office, was languishing - largely vacant except for a few offices occupied by the British Transport Police and with the British Railways Staff Association in a part of the former carriage shed downstairs. It was considered as a location for the new signalbox, but rejected in favour of a steel shed in Gateshead, however in 1993 work began on its repair and adaptation and a railway telesales centre opened there early in 1994.

Plenty of scope still exists to bring other commercial uses into vacant or underused parts of the station on the pattern pursued, sometimes with excessive vigour, in France and Germany. Meanwhile, work is progressing on a long backlog of repairs. British Rail had reclad the Dobson trainshed in 1977-8 with a metal sheeting which gives quite a good approximation to the appearance of the former timber planking. The two southern spans, by William Bell, had been left alone and the southernmost had been badly neglected, with no covering at all on one side of its skylight, resulting in unnecessary decay of the roof timbers and corrosion of the ironwork. This has been remedied in the first phase of a major repair programme undertaken by Railtrack, who became the station's owners in the course of privatisation and have also removed the now-redundant signalbox and reinstated that part of the roof demolished to accommodate it. The roof over Dobson's office range was also in a badly neglected state and has been receiving attention at the same time.

Hopefully, Newcastle Central Station will enter its 150th birthday year in far better fettle than it has been at any time during the last half-century and with every prospect of playing a major role in Tyneside's transport for another 150 years.

Plate 7.1 A view taken about 1905 of the east end diamonds showing the complex crossings built up from flat-bottom rails. Newcastle City Libraries.

Plate 7.2 A view from the Castle keep showing the layout after its simplification in 1904 by the removal of the connections from the HLB to platforms 1 and 2 and the carriage dock. The 1893 to 1909 Newcastle No. 1 box can be seen on the right of the picture. J. F. Addyman collection.

Chapter 7

TRACK AND SIGNALLING

The East End Diamonds

Claims, at the beginning of the twentieth century, that the NER ran the fastest train in the British Empire or owned a larger area of docks than any other railway in the world could be proved. Whether the claim that Newcastle's east end diamonds was the largest or most concentrated junction in the world was true is not known but it does not seem to have been contested. The diamonds came into being in 1893 as a result of the track quadrupling and station extensions being carried out then. The layouts before and after the additional tracks were provided are shown in Fig. 7.1 and page 124

Until 1888, with the exception of a small tonnage of flat-bottom rails used on waybeams on bridges, engine pits, etc., all NER rails were double-headed and intended to be turned over at half-life to provide a new running surface. In 1888 they adopted their 90lb. per yd. bull-head rail for use on their main lines[1]. Bessemer steel rails had first been tested in the North East on the High Level Bridge in April 1862[2] and although the trial was very successful the demand for the harder wearing rails was so great that it was not until 1877 that all new rails purchased by the company were steel rather than wrought iron[3]. In 1876 the process for making cast steel had been introduced by Sir Henry Bessemer (1813-1898).

The first east end diamonds were made up of the bull-head rail and cast steel crossings on normal cross-timbers. Before the whole of the diamonds were renewed for the first time in 1899 some of the cast crossings had already been replaced which suggests they were only mild steel. The sheer volume and weight of traffic was such that the next layout did not even last as long as the first. It had been hoped that something more durable than the cast steel could be provided and it was decided to build up the crossings from flat-bottom rails, rivetted to continuous steel baseplates fixed on 16in. square waybeams[4] A normal diamond is made up of two common, acute or 'V' crossings and two obtuse or 'K' crossings but at Newcastle because of their small size an inner diamond is formed by the continuous check and wing rails and Fig. 7.1 illustrates one of the diamonds as made up for its last renewal in 1970[5]. In 1899 they decided to continue one pair of rails through each intersection and notch or groove their heads to permit the wheel flanges of the cross-traffic to pass through. The cross-rails were butted up against the continuous rails and fastened with special fishplates. The grooves for the flanges were only made 1½in. wide instead of 2in. and because of the severe curvature this resulted in a number of broken rails[6].

By 1904 the crossings were badly out of alignment, worn and due for renewal. The North Tyneside electric service had been introduced that year using platforms 1 and 2 at Central Station and it was decided that access from these platforms and from the east carriage dock to the High Level Bridge was no longer required; this reduced the diamonds by 60 to 70 crossings. The renewal this time was with 104lb. per yard flat-bottom rail and the intersections were properly made up in the normal manner. A refinement was that special cast steel blocks were put in at the nose of each crossing to support the flanges and prevent the wheels from dropping between the nose and wing rails at each intersection where the gap had been increased due to the flangeways being widened from 1½in. to 2in. The rails were again rivetted to the steel baseplates and the waybeams were made up of three 10in. by 5in. pieces of timber bolted together Fig. 7.1. These crossings stood up well to the very heavy traffic and it was not until they had been in for six years that problems with broken rails and bolts became frequent but it was another two years before the next complete renewal was done[7].

Normal railway rails are known as medium manganese and contain a small percentage of manganese which makes them more resistant to wear than mild steel. Further amounts of manganese can be added to the steel without any benefit until the figure exceeds 11 per cent. Rails or castings with 12 to 14 per cent. are known as high manganese and have the property of almost instantaneous work-hardening making an extremely hard wearing material which is also very difficult to machine or drill. Their cost is about five times as much as ordinary steel rails[8]. It was decided that the 1912 renewal should be done in Hadfield's Era cast high manganese steel from Sheffield.

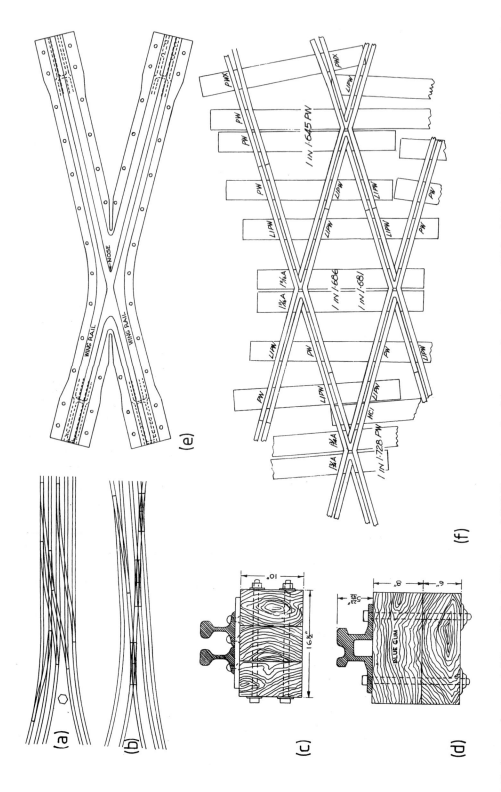

Fig. 7.1 (a) & (b) The layout at the east end of Central Station in 1890 (top) and 1990. The maximum size of the east end diamonds, between 1894 and 1904, is shown on page 124. (c) Section of a built-up crossing prior to 1912 using 104 lb per yd flat-bottom rails rivetted to steel baseplates. Note that the check rail, on the left, has had its foot planed to give the correct flangeway. (d) Section of one of the 1912 high manganese castings showing it through-bolted to waybeams of blue gum and Vancouver pine. (e) A typical design of casting for an acute or common crossing showing the shaping of the nose to minimise damage and wear. (f) One of the built-up diamonds in bull-head material for the 1970 renewal. The numbers indicate the angle of the crossings (e.g. 1 in 1.645) and the letters on the timbers the type of chair (e.g. pw).

B. P. Fletcher (1883-1976) who designed the new layout explained some of the problems with the previous renewals. "Before the opening of the King Edward VII Bridge (in 1906) the renewal of these crossings could only be done piecemeal, as there was no alternative route for traffic, which had to be dealt with over the old High Level Bridge. As this place is one of the busiest in the world, it was only possible to renew a small portion at a time, and since it was necessary to couple it up with existing work at the end of each day, there was no alternative but to reproduce the alignment as it existed. With the excessive traffic, and owing to the crossings being practically all on curves, the alignment became irregular". The new layout was designed and set out with great care to ensure that accurate circular curves and spiral transitions were incorporated[9].

A typical casting and cross section are shown in Fig. 7.1 and their normal weight between intersections was 225lbs. per yd. The flangeway between the running and check rails was made 1¼in. deep to support the wheel flanges in order to prevent damage to the crossing noses which were inclined to ³/₁₆in. below their normal level and specially curved as an additional safeguard. Two layers of bitumastic felt were laid immediately below the castings to take up irregularities and the waybeams were made up of a hardwood, blue gum, on top of a softwood, Vancouver pine. The castings were made to match up to British Standard 95lb. per yd. bull-head rails at their extremities. The layout included 92 crossing and rail castings and used 70 tons of high manganese steel; the total cost was £6,000[10].

The crossings were subsequently renewed in 1924, 1938 and 1949. The 1924 castings were repaired by electric welding after they were removed in 1938 and held in reserve as spares. During the last three to four years prior to the 1949 renewal there were 20 occasions when an old 1924 unit was used as a replacement while repairs to the 1938 sets were carried out. In 1949 the new layout had its insulated joints repositioned, as previously there had been occasions when traffic had not been properly detected by the track circuits. This meant that previous crossings could not be used in cases of emergency and it was decided to have a brand new reserve set manufactured immediately after the new layout had been installed. The 1949 castings were taken out at an estimated half-life in 1956 and the sets were exchanged again in 1963. In 1969 the layout was again reduced in size when the access from platforms 3 and 4 to the High Level Bridge was no longer required. At this time an assessment of the condition of the reserve castings was made and it was found that many had already been used for emergency replacements and further repairs were not possible. The castings in use were not expected to last through the 1970 summer timetable without failures which would have caused severe traffic problems[11]. Quotations were obtained from Osborn-Hadfield and Edgar Allen Ltd. for new castings but they were not ordered as a decision whether or not to keep the tracks over the High Level Bridge had to be made. When they finally opted to retain the tracks it was too late for the castings to be produced before the start of the summer timetable. It was then decided to put the clock back to 1893 and build up the diamonds in bull-head material, on timbers with two complete units, forming five intersections, being produced in cast manganese by Edgar Allen. The reason for using bull-head rail instead of the current standard 113lb. per yd. flat-bottom rail was to avoid the expense and waste of having to plane the feet of the flat-bottom rail to give the correct continuous check rail flangeway. This layout was built up by Taylor Bros. (Sandiacre) Ltd. in April 1970 and installed in two weekends by 24th May[12]. (Steam enthusiasts may be pleased to know that the new diamonds were effectively christened by steam from the cylinder exhaust cocks of preserved streamlined Pacific *Sir Nigel Gresley* a few hours after completion.) A vision of old permanent way designers rattling their chains in horror at the thought of the retrograde step was not justified as the built-up crossings stood up very well to the, now much reduced, volume of traffic. In the track remodelling and resignalling prior to 1991 electrification the diamonds were replaced by just three double-slip switch-diamonds giving an even simpler layout than the 1849 one (Fig. 7.1). This was made possible by removing one of the tracks over the High Level Bridge and one on the Newcastle to Manors viaduct.

Plate 7.3 The 1949 cast manganese layout for the diamonds at the district engineer's yard at Low Fell. It was essential that complex permanent way layouts were pre-assembled to ensure the correct alignment and proper seating on the timbers, which were drilled for the chair screws at this stage. When all was satisfactory it was broken down into sections for transport as an out-of-gauge load to the site. British Railways.

Plate 7.4 The old track and ballast have been removed and the new bottom ballast has been rolled to allow the timber waybeams to be placed on a compacted level bed. Accurate lining and levelling at this stage will considerably extend the crossings' life. At least one of the cranes being used is a breakdown crane which has been borrowed for the day. British Railways.

Plate 7.5 The renewal almost complete with the penultimate cast manganese unit being lowered on to the timbers. British Railways.

Plate 7.6 The completed 1970 built-up layout in bull-head material with sleepers. P. W. Elliston.

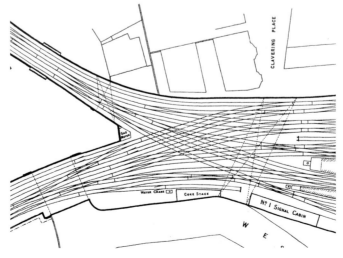

The Diamonds in 1894

Signalling

J. F. MALLON

In the 25 years between the openings of the Stockton and Darlington Railway and Newcastle Central Station great advances had been made in civil and mechanical engineering but railway signalling had remained primitive to say the least. In 1850 signal boxes were virtually unknown and, at best, small huts or shelters were used by the pointsmen or policemen, whose job it was to dash about to set the individual points or signals as few of these were remotely controlled from a lever frame. Semaphore railway signals had first been used in England in 1841 but these were not introduced into the North East until 1852; up to that time the relatively few signals, that there were, had been rotating discs or boards. The interlocking of points and signals to prevent conflicting train movements was first available in England in 1856 but it was over a decade later before the NER started to adopt it to any degree. Trains were dispatched into the "blue yonder" on a time interval system and the 1880s had arrived before block signalling had been completed on all the railways throughout Britain. Block signalling divided each line into blocks or sections which, in the simplest form, were controlled by a "distant" or caution signal and a "home" or stop signal from a signal box. Each box was linked by telegraph to the ones at either side of it and a train could not be accepted into a section until the previous train had cleared it. In very busy locations, such as Newcastle, the railway company could be absolved from working "Absolute Block" with the agreement of the Board of Trade railway inspectorate.

It is impossible to get a complete picture of early signalling as drawings are almost non-existent and the authorisation for many new boxes does not appear in the minutes. T. E. Harrison as Engineer-in-Chief must have had a virtually free hand to carry out the relatively inexpensive signalling installations within his annual permanent way department budget. Board of Trade inspection reports for new installations are also rare and as they did not report on any accident at Newcastle until 1865 there is no early information to be gleaned from that source either. The locations of the numerous boxes referred to in this chapter are given in Figs. 7.2 and 7.3.

1850 to 1868

The first accounts of the 1850s signalling did not appear until the early years of the twentieth century and may compress the facts a little, however with the detail that they do provide, some minute book references and the Ordnance Survey maps of 1857 and 1859, it is possible to get some idea of the situation. From the outset there was one signal immediately outside the trainshed to admit all the main line trains and it was later connected by a wire to a lever on one of the roof columns near the centre of the station; warning of approaching trains was given by the signalman at the High Level Bridge ringing a bell. Other early signals mentioned were starting ones for trains leaving the station and home and distants for trains arriving plus a solitary one on the goods lines. In 1850 all the points were hand operated by adjacent levers and safety devices like facing point locks were almost 20 years ahead. Some of the more important points had a heavy balance weight attached to their point levers to keep them set for the main route; to allow passage on the minor route in the facing direction the lever had to be held over but in the trailing direction the points could be forced over by the wheels against the restraint of the balance weight. In 1850 there were 96 trains in and out of the station, on weekdays, and three pointsmen and two assistants worked all the points and signals.

The 1865 accident report refers to the three east end signal boxes rather disparagingly as "Huts 1, 2 and 3". The octagonal Hut 1 must date from before August 1854 because it was used as a prototype for the box then authorised to control the lines into York station. The box had two signals mounted on opposite faces and housed levers which controlled all the nearby points by rodding. It probably replaced a shelter which the pointsman had used between working the individual points and signal levers. On 22nd March 1855 the Locomotive Committee let the contract for £250 to build "a signalmen's cabin and ticket collectors' office". This building, Hut 2, was considerably revised in its execution and it seems probable that the ticket collectors accommodation was abandoned and the whole structure was used for signalling purposes. Weighted levers were retained on many of the nearby points so, unlike Hut 1, it did not remotely control all those in its locality. In 1857 Hut 3 was still the original basic shelter with four uncovered point levers to the east of it and a signal immediately to the west of it which probably controlled all the trains entering the station. No details are known of the early Newcastle and

Plate 7.7 The original 1872 No. 3 cabin at the east end of Central Station shown about 1893 during the work for the enlargement of the station. The extensions made at each end to accommodate the increase in levers from 57 to 87 can be seen above the girders. The contemporary No. 2 or Central box is just visible to the left of the rear wagons behind the crane. Newcastle City Libraries.

Plate 7.8 Looking south-east at No. 1 E.P. box at the east end of Central in the 1950s. Hugh Murray collection.

Carlisle signalling arrangements at Central Station other than the provision of a cabin, similar to Hut 3, and situated near Forth Banks bridge. From the large scale Ordnance Survey it is evident that there were no weighted point levers and with the much simpler track layout and less frequent train movements it is possible that few of the point levers would have been concentrated in the cabin itself.

By 1858 the next boxes on the main line beyond Hut 1 were Manors Junction on the line to Heaton and High Level Bridge South Junction on the line to Darlington. Manors Junction controlled the main line and access to Trafalgar goods station while High Level Bridge South Junction controlled the main line to Darlington. The NER regulated trains using a time interval of five minutes (Rule 137) but in 1858 due to the growth in traffic this rule had to be suspended for trains between Central Station and Manors and over the High Level Bridge.

1868 to 1871

In 1868 the Team Valley line opened from Durham and Team Valley Junction cabin, later renamed Gateshead Junction, was provided at the south end of the High Level Bridge. This cabin was on the centre of a bridge or gantry spanning the tracks but to improve visibility it was replaced, after 1876, by a smaller box on the east end of the girders. By 1871 Hut 3 had been replaced by something larger and contained a lever frame with interlocking although weighted levers still remained in use on a number of nearby points; Hut 1 still had no interlocking at this time.

1871 to 1881

All this was about to change, however, as the station was being remodelled to include an additional island platform. This gave the opportunity to modernise the control of the station and four new signal boxes were built in 1871-72. No 1 was an octagonal cabin in the middle of the station at the head of, the then, platform 3; No 2, or "Central" box, was a bridge cabin spanning that platform, 50 yards beyond the end of the trainshed roof; No 3 was a bridge cabin, also known as "Castle Junction", spanning all the tracks at the station throat; "Forth Banks Junction", another octagonal box, replaced the Newcastle and Carlisle cabin and lever frame at the west end. No 1 controlled all the lines within the station and three of its signals were interlocked with No 2 to regulate admission to the platforms. No 2 controlled 15 points leading to the loading docks and platform lines, a connection from, the then, platform 8 to the engine shed on the south side of the station and 21 signals were worked from it. No 3 was by far the largest of the new cabins, with a 57-lever locking frame which worked 15 points and 34 signals; it was later enlarged to accommodate an 87-lever frame. This resignalling was begun in the spring of 1871 but not completed until July-August 1872. The boxes were open continuously and an accident report of June 1876 reveals that there were then about 7,000 lever movements daily in No 3 box alone. Sometime after the beginning of November 1877 another bridge cabin was built above pier No 5 of the High Level Bridge, from which it took its name. Its signals provided advance warning to drivers approaching Castle Junction, as did those of yet another bridge cabin, Pilgrim Street, mounted on the viaduct east of the Dean Street arch (opened September-October 1874). These new boxes created shorter sections, adding to safety and increasing line capacity.

In the early 1870s the block system was rapidly being introduced on all NER lines, together with T. E. Harrison's facing point locks. At Newcastle, telegraphic bell codes, describing all the trains, were in use between all the boxes by the mid 1870s. By the end of 1878 the full block working had been extended from Manors Junction to Pilgrim Street but was not used at Central Station. Newcastle No 1 became the key to the working of trains into and out of the station and by the end of 1881 was under the direct supervision of the station master or his day and night assistants. Arriving trains were signalled by bell codes from the other station boxes to No 1 whose signalman decided which platform they should enter and he informed them of his decision by using electrical indicators; each of the signal boxes had a set of these indicators, one for each platform. A novel system of interlocking by wire connections between Nos 2 and 3 boxes controlled their levers as if they were all concentrated in one box. Two inches of movement of a lever in either box made the interlocking action. The arrangements in No 1 box were such that if the arrival signal was given to a box for a train routed to one of the three through platforms, the electrical indicators were interlocked to prevent an arrival signal being given to the other boxes at the same time. Forth Banks Junction was replaced about 1880 by a splay cornered box.

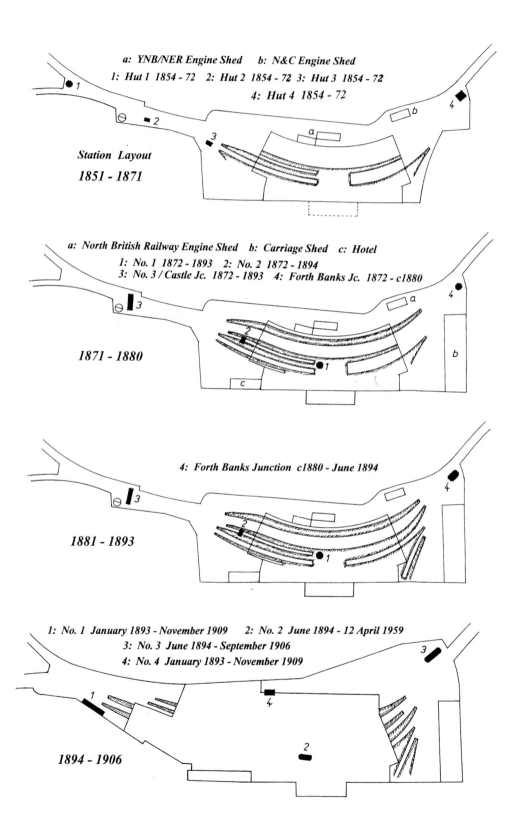

a: YNB/NER Engine Shed   b: N&C Engine Shed

1: Hut 1 1854 - 72   2: Hut 2 1854 - 72   3: Hut 3 1854 - 72

4: Hut 4 1854 - 72

Station Layout

1851 - 1871

a: North British Railway Engine Shed   b: Carriage Shed   c: Hotel

1: No. 1 1872 - 1893   2: No. 2 1872 - 1894

3: No. 3 / Castle Jc. 1872 - 1893   4: Forth Banks Jc. 1872 - c1880

1871 - 1880

4: Forth Banks Junction c1880 - June 1894

1881 - 1893

1: No. 1 January 1893 - November 1909   2: No. 2 June 1894 - 12 April 1959

3: No. 3 June 1894 - September 1906

4: No. 4 January 1893 - November 1909

1894 - 1906

128

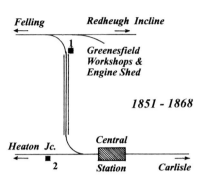

1851 - 1868

1: High Level Bridge South Junction c1857 - 11/1868
2: Manors Junction c1857 - 12/6/1887

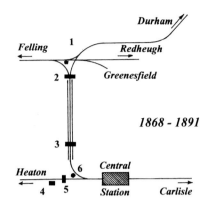

1868 - 1891

1: Greenesfield 1868 - 9/12/1962
2: Gateshead Junction 1868 - 1892
3: High Level bridge after 1/11/1877 - 6/1887
4: Manors Junction 12/6/1887 - 1891
5: Pilgrim Street 10/1874 - 12/6/1887
6: Octagon 12/6/1887 - 1891

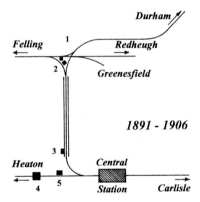

1891 - 1906

1: Greenesfield 1868 - 9/12/1962
2: Gateshead Junction 1892 - 4/1930
3: High Level Bridge c1891 - 11/1909
4: Manors Junction 1891 - 11/1908
5: Dean Street 1891 - 11/1909

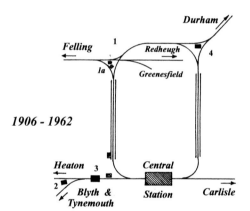

1906 - 1962

1: Greenesfield 1868 - 9/12/1962
1a: Gateshead Junction 1892 - 1930
2: Manors 6/1943 - 12/4/1959
3: Manors Junction 11/1908 - 13/6/1943
4: King Edward Bridge Junction 9/1906 - 9/12/1962

Fig. 7.3 (above) The evolution of the approach routes and their signalboxes from 1851 to 1962.

Fig. 7.2 (left and below) The development of Central Station and its signalboxes from 1851 to 1959.

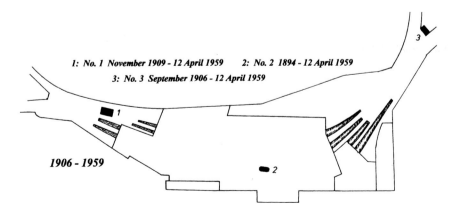

1: No. 1 November 1909 - 12 April 1959   2: No. 2 1894 - 12 April 1959
3: No. 3 September 1906 - 12 April 1959

1906 - 1959

Plate 7.9 Interior of Newcastle No. 1 E.P. box about 1930 showing the block and train describer instruments on the left and the miniature lever frame on the right. Newcastle City Libraries.

Plate 7.10 A view of the west end taken about 1894 showing the 1880 to 1894 Forth Banks Junction box on the left and the 1894 to 1906 No. 3 box on the right. K. L. Taylor collection.

1881 to 1891

In 1887 a major improvement was completed with the opening of two extra tracks between Manors and Heaton on 1st April and additional platforms at Manors Station on 13th June. In readiness for this Pilgrim Street box was replaced by a new "Octagon" box which opened on 12th June on the site of the original Hut 1. This new box also replaced High Level Bridge box (on pier 5 of the bridge). At the same time a replacement Manors Junction box opened at the west end of the new island platform (platforms 2 and 3) of Manors Station.

Octagon and Manors Junction were intended as an interim measure and were replaced after only four years in 1891. To accommodate the extension of four tracks from Manors to Central, a new Manors Junction box, a 50-lever bridge cabin, was built on the viaduct near Manor Chare while a 30-lever box, Dean Street, was cantilevered from the south side of the viaduct over the adjacent track. Another cantilever box sprouted at the north end of the High Level Bridge; it had 30 levers and replaced Octagon, while at the opposite end of the bridge the Gateshead Junction cabin was replaced in 1892 by a 22-lever box on the down platform of Gateshead East Station.

1891 to 1906

The enlargement of Central Station was completed in phases in 1893 and 1894 and required total resignalling. Two new boxes, Numbers 1 and 4, opened in January 1893 and the others, Numbers 2 and 3, in June 1894, a month before the completion of the widening from Manors. No 1 was much larger than any box hitherto built at Newcastle and one of the largest in Britain, housing 244 levers in a large stone cabin alongside Westgate Road. No 3 was a splay-cornered stone cabin replacing the Forth Banks Junction box on the opposite side of the tracks, while No 4 was cantilevered out on both sides of the rear wall of the newly extended trainshed. No 2 had 72 levers, No 3 had 140 and No 4 had 90.

Improvements to safety were introduced in February 1895, when recording block instruments were installed in Gateshead Junction and High Level Bridge to show the number of trains standing on all the lines between them in each direction. In June 1895 they were added in Dean Street and Manors, and in May 1898 in No 3 for trains to and from the West.

1906 to 1959

The 1893-94 resignalling had a life of just 12 years before the need to resignal the west end of Central Station, to accommodate the King Edward Bridge, gave an opportunity to update the whole installation to the electro-pneumatic (E.P.) system. This had been done at five boxes at Tyne Dock, beginning in 1902, and had proved extremely successful in dealing with that area's very heavy, predominantly mineral, traffic.

In the E.P. system, the large heavy mechanical levers were replaced by miniature levers operating solenoid valves which admitted compressed air to pneumatic motors moving the points and signals. This considerably reduced the physical effort required by the signalmen and also extended the maximum distance from the box to points to 50 yards more than the 250 yards stipulated for manual operation. A compressor supplied air at 65 to 70lbs. per sq. in. to individual storage tanks near each signal box.

The first E.P. boxes opened in connection with the King Edward Bridge. At its south end, King Edward Bridge Junction, with 83 levers, came into use shortly before the formal opening of the bridge on 10th July 1906. Because the alterations to the west end of the station were still under way, the bridge did not open to traffic until 1st October, the new cabin controlling the west end, No 3, being commissioned on 2nd September. This box was built on to the corner of Forth goods station and had 211 levers, train describers and recording block indicators. The only existing structure to be retained was No 2, which was converted to E.P. operation in March 1907; it had 67 levers. Boxes 1 and 4 together with High Level Bridge and Dean Street cabins, were replaced by the largest of the Newcastle E.P. boxes, a new No 1, brought into use during 7th to 12th November 1909. This was a bridge cabin with 283 levers, straddling the lines at the east end of the main line platforms (8 to 10). The Dean Street cabin was retained to house the circuit breakers for the suburban electric trains.

Electro-pneumatic operation came to Manors Junction with the provision of a replacement cabin on the opposite side of the supporting girders from the previous box; the new cabin had 43 levers and opened in November 1908. Across the Tyne, Greensfield Junction was converted to E.P. operation in December 1906, with 55 levers, and Gateshead Junction in June 1907 with 23 levers.

Plate 7.11 The 1906 Newcastle No. 3 E.P. box built on to the corner of the Forth Goods Station. The lines to the left are on the approach to the King Edward Bridge and the original Newcastle to Carlisle route is on the right. Hugh Murray collection.

Plate 7.12 A signalman's view of the track layout at the west end of Central Station controlled by No. 3 box, seen in the 1950s. Hugh Murray collection.

A feature of E.P. operation was that all the lines were track-circuited, showing track occupation on illuminated diagrams in all the boxes. There was extensive use of calling-on arms which were placed below the stop signals. If a train was already in the section ahead, the stop signal remained at danger, and the calling-on arm was lowered to permit a driver to proceed with caution to carry out shunting or engine changing movements. Route indicators were fixed on some signals. With the opening of the new No 1 box modified block regulations came into effect, but there was no block working between Nos 1, 2 and 3 and electric bells continued to signal trains between them. Tyers Train Describers were also provided, indicating details of each train.

Before World War I centralised train control was only found on the NER at Middlesbrough, where it had been introduced in 1910 to deal with a heavy and diverse freight traffic. Wartime brought a vast increase in goods traffic and a freight control office was established at Central Station on 3rd December 1917 ". . . to facilitate generally the working of freight traffic by having all the information as to the position of traffic and trains concentrated in one place". Later, all passenger trains were controlled in the same way.

The financial conditions prevailing after the war, and the general strike of 1926 led to a permanent loss of revenue causing the LNER to make economies in all departments. In April 1930 Gateshead Junction box closed, and its duties were transferred to Greensfield Junction. During the 1930s the LNER embarked on replacing semaphore signals with colour lights on the former NER section of the East Coast Main Line, completing the changeover between York (Skelton) and Darlington on the day World War 2 broke out - 3rd September 1939. By the mid-thirties some colour light shunting signals and stop signals with route indicators were appearing at Newcastle No 1 and Manors. On 13th December 1937 further colour lights were introduced between No 1 box and Manors, providing for two-way working on each of the two main line tracks.

On 13th June 1943 Manors box was destroyed by fire and temporary hand-signalling, with flags, was brought in; train routing was carried out by No 1 box using the Dean Street crossovers. By the end of the month a temporary box was in place at the west end of Manors' platforms 7 and 8, controlling the North main lines only. The Tynemouth lines were connected to it on 8th July and normal working resumed; a permanent box was eventually provided just to the east.

1959 to 1999

Planning for the replacement of the E.P. boxes by a single all-electric one was begun by the LNER about 1937, with a projected completion of about 1945. Some equipment had been manufactured by the contractors, the Westinghouse Brake and Signal Co., by the time World War 2 began when all work on the contract stopped. After the war planning re-started and was continued by B.R. after nationalisation, on 1st January 1948, but a priority on the North Eastern Region was the resignalling of York, whose new box opened in 1951. The new Newcastle box did not come into use until 12th April 1959, replacing Nos 1, 2 and 3 and Manors. It was housed on the upper floor of the island platform offices and extended from there across platform 10 and the adjoining lines to emerge as a huge gable from the rear wall of the trainshed; most of this space was occupied by the relay room and cabling.

Some of the semaphore signals had already been replaced by colour lights, for example, around 1950 the large gantry beside No 1 was replaced as a prelude to the modernisation. When the remaining ones were replaced there was a total of 94 two, three or four aspect running signals, 61 having route indicators; 86 shunting signals showed a red and white light for "stop" and two white lights at 45 degrees for "proceed"; 84 subsidiary signals were normally dark, and had a "C" calling-on sign in place of the red light. The 131 sets of points remained operated by compressed air but had new motors.

The control room contained the switch console with route-relay interlocking and the illuminated track diagram, in four sections, each with a signalman. There were 641 switches on the console to set up the routes, and train describer display indicators, which gave the description and destination of a train above the route diagram, were set by push-buttons..

When a route was set up, it was lit up in white by a number of the 2,840 route lights set into the diagram. These remained lit until the train had passed and the route was restored to normal. Flashing green lights indicated a train ready to depart and were activated by a plunger on each platform; these lights were extinguished when the appropriate starting signal was cleared. Telephones connected certain signals, adjacent signal boxes and the control office. A traffic regulator sat at a raised desk where he could supervise all that was happening at the console. The train announcer's booth was also included in the signal box.

By the 1980s, this equipment was coming to the end of its economic life. A site at the west end of Chaytor's Bank, in Gateshead, between the railway and Askew Road and outside the scope of this history, was selected for the new building; this was fitted with the most up-to-date electronic equipment including seven computer workstations. It opened on 12th April 1991, exactly 32 years after its predecessors, is known as "Tyneside" signal box, but is also referred to as the Tyneside Integrated Electronic Control Centre (IECC). In connection with it, many of the tracks and routes in the station were simplified or removed, whilst two new additional through platforms have been added.

In the triangle of the lines at the Gateshead side of the High Level Bridge, a more modern box than Newcastle opened on 9th December 1962. This took over the work of Greensfield and King Edward Bridge, and itself was superseded by Tyneside IECC. In contrast to Huts 1, 2 and 3 which together controlled less than a quarter of a mile of railway the new box controls from south of Darlington to south of Morpeth.

Plate 7.13   The interior of No. 3 E.P. box showing the miniature levers and diagram of the lines controlled.   Cyril Myton.

Plate 7.14   The interior of the 1959 Newcastle box showing from top to bottom: the train describer panel and the illuminated track diagram, with the switch console below. Cyril Myton.

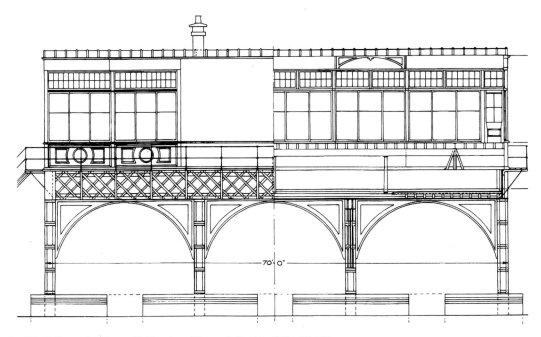

Fig. 7.4. Half rear elevation and half section of Newcastle No. 1 in 1909. J.F. Addyman

134

Appendix 1

ROAD AND RAILWAY SCHEMES FOR BRIDGING THE RIVER TYNE BETWEEN GATESHEAD AND NEWCASTLE: 1771-1844

R. W. RENNISON

First published in 'The High Level Bridge, Newcastle' by R. W. Rennison, in *Transactions of the Newcomen Society*, volume 52, 1980-81.

Road Bridges

1. Edward Hutchinson, 1771
2. Captain Samuel Brown, 1826
3. William Chapman, 1826
4. Robert Stevenson, 1828
5. Barrodal Robert Dodd, 1834
9. William Martin, 1836
13. John & Benjamin Green, 1839
15. Richard Grainger, 1843
16. John Dobson, 1843
17. John & Benjamin Green, 1843

Railway Bridges

6. Robert Nicholson, 1835
7. Richard Grainger & Thomas Sopwith, 1836
8. Great North of England Railway, 1836
9. William Martin, 1836
10. Great North of England Railway, 1837
11. John Bourne, 1837
12. Northern Union Railway, 1839
14. John & Benjamin Green, 1841
18. Robert William Brandling, 1844
19. Isambard Kingdom Brunel, 1844

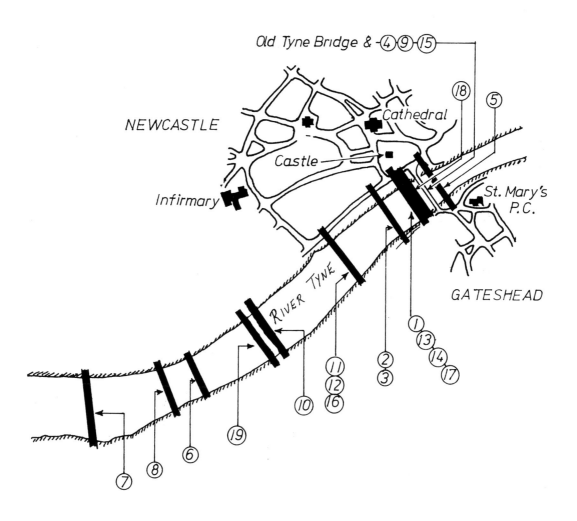

Appendix 2 (a)

RIDSDALE IRON WORKS

Dr. I. D. Roberts

Ridsdale Iron Works near West Woodburn in Redesdale was the place where approximately 15% of the iron used in Newcastle's High Level Bridge was first manufactured. Few traces, other than the ruined engine house, remain of these works despite the fact that the iron once produced was of extremely high quality. Under these circumstances and additionally as previous published accounts of the operations of these works are frequently factually erroneous, it is appropriate in the context of this book to provide a short history of the works. The account which follows has been based on original evidence drawn from papers in the Duke of Northumberland's archives at Alnwick Castle, oral evidence given to Parliamentary Select Committees to be found in the House of Lords' Record Office and material in the Northumberland Record Office. The author is grateful for permission to consult these sources. For reference, the principal earlier articles are listed at the end of this appendix.

The increasing demand by a variety of industries for metals of all types as a result of growing industrialisation in England led to the exploration of the remoter areas of the country for exploitable mineral resources. During the late eighteenth and early nineteenth centuries, prospectors of coal, lead, iron and other minerals began to search North Tynedale and Redesdale for evidence of commercial quantities of these materials, the presence of which had been known since medieval times. In the late 1830s, large deposits of coal and iron were found, located close to each other, in the valley of the Hareshaw Burn near the village of Bellingham and also south of West Woodburn at the eastern end of the valley of the Chesterhope Burn. In the case of the latter, a group of local men headed by two landowners, Thomas Hedley and Stephen Reed, formed the Chesterhope Iron Company to manufacture pig iron. In 1838 they obtained from the Duke of Northumberland a lease of mineral rights to extract iron and coal. The proposed site of the works, part of the present village of Ridsdale, which was already in the ownership of the company, was an area of totally undeveloped common land that had been enclosed as recently as 1807. The lease the company took on the mineral rights was for twenty-one years with a certain rent of £125 per annum for the first three years and £300 thereafter. Royalties were to be charged for ironstone, coal, limestone and fire clay. In 1839 a single blast furnace with a steam-powered blast was installed and pig iron produced.

It should be stressed that the Ridsdale operation began on what was a green field site adjacent to the Corbridge to Carter Bar turnpike road (now A68). In addition, West Woodburn, situated two miles from Ridsdale, was then only a small village with very few available houses, while the nearby farming hamlet of Chesterhope had only one vacant residential property so the company not only had to erect the ironworks but also had to build houses for the majority of its workers. By late 1839 the company appeared to be in some financial difficulties, probably arising from development expenses and difficulties in marketing and processing the pig iron being produced. In consequence the company was offered to J. Richardson, W. Richardson, Bigge and Cargill, who had recently invested £10,000 to form the Derwent Iron Company, in County Durham. Initially they were reluctant to involve themselves with Ridsdale, but by January 1840 a local Land Agent reported that "a new respectable company" had taken control at Ridsdale, paying £30,000 for so doing.

Of the four partners, it was Bigge who took charge at Ridsdale as Acting Manager. In the following year he erected two more blast furnaces, enlarging the village in the process, and increased the production of iron by introducing, as far as can be determined, the hot blast method of smelting. The iron produced at Ridsdale was sent to the company's works at Bishopwearmouth for refining and was then sold as part of the company's overall output.

It would seem that the Ridsdale iron works initially made sound progress, but was affected adversely by the recession in the iron trade in 1842 and 1843 as in both years the company had to apply to the Duke's agent for remission in royalties. The company's fortunes must have revived, as there was no further demand for relief for the next three years. In 1846 the success of the Ridsdale works as the producer of the strongest iron in the tests carried out by Robert Stephenson at the Gateshead foundry led to the sale of significant quantities for use as an alloy in the High Level Bridge. From contemporary evidence, the success of Ridsdale iron was not surprising, James Smith, who managed the Ridsdale works at the time, stated a few years later that the iron he produced was of better quality than hot or cold blast iron from South Wales and the equal of that produced at Low Moor, near Bradford, "the best in the Kingdom".

Unfortunately the successes of 1846 were not repeated in the following year as sales deteriorated to the point where the Duke was approached once more to change the terms of the lease. The Duke's agents considered the company's affairs in some detail, reporting that by this stage some £160,000 had been invested in the works at Ridsdale. The agents offered a number of reductions in the royalty payments, clearly in an effort to protect a valuable source of income as in the year to September 1847 the company had paid £2,226 12s 1d in rent and royalties. The agents also suggested that the company might consider expanding its operation to include the manufacture of some malleable iron at the works. Despite the necessity of finding a further capital sum of £10,000 to accomplish this, the company accepted the suggestion and by May 1848 began to produce malleable iron at Ridsdale. The Duke's agents reported that the workforce was very satisfied with the quality of the new product, but were concerned that their principal supply of coal from the pit on Aid Crag had only about nine months supply before it would be exhausted.

Permission was given to open a new pit, but the initial cost of the work must have sounded the death knell for the company. During the process of sinking the new shaft, iron founding was abandoned and the works effectively closed. The workers must have dispersed very shortly afterwards as the 1851 Census shows no records of iron miners or workers living in any part of the parish to which Ridsdale belonged. At the same time no further approaches were made to the Duke until January 1852 when an agent of the company wrote to the Duke stating that the company was to be sold and offering him first refusal on the property. The Duke declined and the works were sold to a Mr Forster.

Forster was an employee of the Derwent Iron Company and then of its successor, the Consett Iron Company. As such he possessed a considerable knowledge of iron founding and in due course approached the Duke to negotiate a fresh lease on the mineral rights at Ridsdale as part of a new scheme to manufacture iron. A lease was drawn up in 1860 and Forster set about raising the £14,000 he required to commence operations. Not only did he fail to do this, but died shortly afterwards, leaving the works and associated land to be disposed of by his executors at public auction. Although no sale took place at the auction, a private treaty sale was arranged shortly afterwards. The purchaser, W. G. Armstrong, the armaments manufacturer from Elswick on Tyneside became the possessor of the works, the village and over 180 acres of land for £3,500.

There is little doubt that Armstrong gained a bargain. The sale advertisement shows the extent of the investment at Ridsdale. There were three blast furnaces, engine houses, foundries, blacksmith's and joiner's shops and over 120 houses. Armstrong dismantled the furnaces and re-erected them at Elswick. Using the newly opened railway to the valley, he extracted and calcined ore for carriage to Tyneside where it was processed for the manufacture of high quality shells. This work was begun in 1864 and discontinued in 1880 when the importation of cheaper Spanish iron ore made it uneconomic, thus bringing to a close an interesting chapter in the economic history of the Rede valley.

Remoteness of location and expense of transport played some part in contributing to the failure of the Ridsdale iron works, despite the superior quality of its product. There is, however, more to the story than it is possible to explain in this appendix. Only when full account has been taken of the size of capital investment in the plant and associated village, the company's management strategies, which were notoriously bad according to some observers, the nature of the technology employed and the difficulties of recruiting and training a work force will it be possible to reconstruct the complete circumstances of the rise and decline of this erstwhile ambitious enterprise.

References:

T. M. Hoskison, "Northumberland Blast Furnace Plants in the Nineteenth Century" in *Transactions of the Newcomen Society* (Vol. XXV 1945-47) 73-81.

R. F. Tylecote, "Recent research on nineteenth century Northumbrian blast furnace sites" in *Industrial Archaeology* (Vol. VIII 1971) 341-359.

S. M. Linsley, "Hareshaw and Ridsdale Ironworks" in *Northumbriana* (Nos.12 and 13, 1978) 15-17 and 11-14.

R. Charlton, "Ridsdale and Vickers" in *Redewetter* (No. 4, 1980) 8-15.

Appendix 2 (b)

Robert Stephenson's letter printed in Appendix 4 of the 1849 Report stated that as a result of the Gateshead experiments he had reached the following conclusions:

"1. Hot Blast less certain in its results than Cold Blast.
2. Mixtures of Cold Blast more uniform than those of Hot Blast.
3. Mixtures of Hot and Cold Blast give best results.
4. Simple samples do not run so solid as mixtures.
5. Simple samples sometimes run too hard, and sometimes too soft, for practical purposes."

"The mixture of iron selected for the arch ribs of the High Level Bridge:

Ystalyfera, No. 3-Anthracite	19% *
Ridsdale, No. 3-Hot Blast	19%
Crawshay (Welsh), No. 1-Cold Blast	19%
Blaenavon, No. 1-Cold Blast	14%
Coalbrookdale, No. 1-Cold Blast	14%
Scrap, selected (clean)	14%

The scrap iron used was principally old mill castings, such as shafts, hammers, rolls, etc., chiefly of Welsh Cold Blast iron".

*Approximate percentages

Appendix 3

High Level Bridge - Dimensions, Cost, etc.
(based on figures quoted by R. Stephenson, R. Hodgson and E. Clark)

Length, including approaches	1340'	8"	(408.6m)
Height, from high water level (1849) to rails	109'	1½"	(33.3m)
Height, from high water level (1849) to carriageway	86'	6"	(26.4m)
Piers-centre to centre	138'	10"	(42.3m)
Span between piers	124'	10"	(38.0m)
Rise of cast iron arch ribs	17'	6"	(5.3m)
Area of foundation to piers	76' 6" (23.3m) by	22' 6"	(6.9m)
Area of shaft of piers	45' 10" (14.0m) by	14' 0"	(4.3m)
Width of carriageway	20'	4"	(6.2m)
Width of footways	6'	2"	(1.9m)

Masonry quantities

	Ashlar	*Rubble*	*Concrete*
Abutments and approaches	360,222 cu.ft.	92,718 cu.ft.	-
	(10,194 cu.m)	(2,624 cu.m)	-
Five river piers	321,387 cu. ft.	23,678 cu. ft.	46,224 cu. ft.
	(9,095 cu.m)	670 cu.m)	(1,308 cu. m)

Iron

Total weight of cast iron	4,728½	tons
Total weight of wrought iron	321½	tons
	5,050	tons
Weight of cast iron in one span	517	tons
Weight of wrought iron in one span	50	tons
Weight of woodwork, paving, etc., in one span	193	tons
Total for one span	760	tons

Cost

	£
Masonry, including coffer-dams	119,000
Iron work, including road, railway, etc.	114,000
Temporary bridge	10,000
	243,000
Total cost of project including Newcastle viaduct and land purchase	491,000

FOOTNOTES

Abbreviations

ICE   Institution of Civil Engineers
NCRO   Northumberland County Record Office (Gosforth)
NRM   National Railway Museum (York)
PRO   Public Records Office (Kew)
TWA   Tyne and Wear Archives (Newcastle)

Chapter 1

1 Horse-drawn wagons running on wooden rails were employed at Sir Francis Willoughby's Wollaton Estate, near Nottingham, to convey coal from his mines to the River Trent. Charles E. Lee in *'The Evolution of Permanent Way'*, published by the Permanent Way Institution in 1937 (reprinted 1992), mentioned a manuscript of 1610 which referred to 'bringing coals down the rails' as well as references to rails in Willoughby's coal accounts for 1597-8.

2 The extent of these individual colliery waggonways is shown in John Gibson's 1787 *Plan of the Collieries on the Rivers Tyne and Wear*, published by the University of Newcastle in Archive Teaching Unit No. 3 - *Railways in the Making* (1969) and edited by R.M. Gard and J.R. Hartley.

3 NCRO: Deposited Plan surveyed by William Chapman in July 1796.

4 NCRO: Newcastle & Carlisle Railway Deposited Plans 1825 & 1828.

5 PRO Rail 509/2 N&C Board 22 January 1830.

6 PRO Rail 509/4 N&C Board 28 May & 26 June 1833. Blackmore had been sent by Giles as his 'Principal Assistant' in April 1830; he oversaw the completion of the N&C and succeeded George Stephenson as engineer to the Maryport & Carlisle Railway. Blackmore remained consulting engineer to the N&C until his untimely death in March 1844, aged 42. Giles's role as consulting engineer from 1833 was largely restricted to negotiations with the Exchequer Loan Board.

7 This suspension bridge, designed by Captain (Sir) Samuel Brown and built under the supervision of John Green, the Newcastle architect and civil engineer, opened in 1831 and was needlessly destroyed following the opening of a new road bridge in 1967. With Scotswood Road it provided a new route into Newcastle from the west.

8 Newcastle Town Council 5 September 1866: the Tyne Improvement Commission served notice of closing the bridge from 17 September, with a temporary wooden bridge coming into use pending construction of the new one.

9 Dimensions and dates for Mylne's Tyne Bridge are taken from Eneas Mackenzie's *'Descriptive and Historical Account of Newcastle and Gateshead'*, pub. 1827.

10 R.W. Rennison 'The High Level Bridge at Newcastle', *Transactions of the Newcomen Society* Vol. 52 (1980-81), p. 180.

11 Another piggy-back scheme, proposed by Richard Grainger in 1843.

12 Born in 1792, John Clayton became town clerk of Newcastle in 1822 in succession to his father, Nathaniel, who had held the post since 1785. John held office until 1867, and continued to pursue an avid interest in the Roman Wall from his country house at Chesters until his death in 1890. He was a leading figure in the Newcastle & Carlisle Railway and many other enterprises, a great facilitator working behind the scenes and, for a time in the eighteen-forties, a keen supporter of George Hudson.

13 The best general accounts of Grainger's work are *'Tyneside Classical'* by Lyall Wilkes and Gordon Dodds, published in 1964, and *'A City of Palaces'* by Ian Ayris, pub. 1997 and incorporating recent scholarship.

14 A good account of the Forth and the Hospital of the Blessed Virgin Mary was given by Mackenzie op. cit.

15 Details from Deposited Plans of the Blaydon, Gateshead & Hebburn Railway.-TWA 285/590.

16 PRO Rail 55/1 BGH Board and shareholders' meetings.

17 PRO Rail 509 N&C Board 21 October 1834.

18 The main sources for the Brandling Junction Railway are: Prospectus of 'Brandling's Junction Railway' (1835), prospectus for the Brandling Junction Railway, and *'An account of the formation of the Brandling Junction Railway'* by Robert William Brandling, all in Newcastle Central Library Local Tracts volume D 29, together with *'A brief history of the Brandling Junction Railway by a late shareholder'* (1845) in volume C45. A few company records are in PRO Rail 64/8. Other accounts are in W.W. Tomlinson *'The North Eastern Railway - Its Rise and Development'*, published in 1914, and F.W.D. Manders *'A History of Gateshead'*, published by Gateshead Corporation in 1973 on the eve of local government reorganisation.

19 A brief account of Storey's S&D career appears in Bill Fawcett 'The Engineers of the Stockton & Darlington Railway', *North Eastern Express* (Journal of the North Eastern Railway Association), vol. 37 no. 151 (1998).

20 PRO Rail 232/2 Great North of England Railway Board 19 August 1836.

21 ibid. 2 September 1836.

22 After prolonged neglect, Elswick Hall was demolished about 1980; the present swimming pool marks its site.

23 PRO Rail 232/2 GNER Board 13 October 1836.

24 ibid. 21 November and 5 December 1837. The GNER Board considered a joint report on the Tyne crossing by Storey, T.E. Harrison (Durham Junction) and Nicholas Wood (Brandling Junction) but resolved, since they had no intention of abandoning the Parliamentary line through County Durham, not to negotiate on the basis proposed by the other railways though remaining open to suggestions regarding the Tyne bridge.

25 An account of GNER problems can be found in Bill Fawcett 'The Great North of England Railway', *North Eastern Express*, vol. 30 nos. 122 & 123 (1991).

26 PRO Rail 509 N&C Board 1 June 1841.

27 Newcastle Courant 4 April 1829.

28 ibid. 30 October 1830 and 23 July 1831.

29 Proc. ICE vol. XIII (1853-4) p. 138.-Obituary of John Green.

30 ibid. vol. I (1841) p. 88; also reported at length in the Civil Engineer & Architect's Journal, February 1848, along with the Dinting Vale viaduct of the Sheffield, Ashton-under-Lyne & Manchester Railway, which copied the Greens' designs.

31 Newcastle Courant 20 August 1836. Advertisement stating 'drawings of the bridges over the Ouseburn and Willington Dene will be ready by Monday 12 September'.

32 PRO Rail 772/3 Newcastle & Darlington Junction Railway Board - A preliminary meeting at York on 6 September 1841, with Hudson in the chair, saw representatives of the Midland Counties, North Midland, York & North Midland, Great North of England, Durham Junction, Brandling Junction and Newcastle & Carlisle Railways approve Robert Stephenson's route and a capitalisation of £500,000, and agree to lease the line for ten years, guaranteeing an annual rent sufficient to return 6% on capital and each receiving shares in proportion to their fraction of the guarantee. The Manchester & Leeds Railway, entering the route at Normanton, later joined the guarantors.

33 TWA 285/290 Prospectus and plan, 1839.

34 Newcastle Town Council 20 December 1843.

35 These alternatives were put to the N&C Board 19 December 1843. On 16 January 1844 they resolved to proceed with a Parliamentary Bill for the bridge, but dropped it the following month after discussions with Hudson.

36 PRO Rail 772/71 contains minutes of a meeting of promoters of the Greens' bridge on 20 September 1843. A letter from the N&DJ (on behalf of all the railways concerned south of the Tyne) guaranteed 3% p.a. on the cost of the bridge and its approaches as a composition for the toll on railway traffic only. This evidently meant road traffic linking railway termini either side of the river, rather than trains.

37 PRO Rail 772/3 N& DJ Board 9 November 1843 - the minutes record in full George Stephenson's letter, written at Tapton House, Chesterfield and beginning: 'Robert has been here and I have learned a great deal from him about the high level bridge intended to connect Newcastle with Gateshead.'

38 Gateshead Observer 22 June 1844 gave details of the Act, including properties needed for the site of the bridge.

39 W.W. Tomlinson op. cit. p. 295.

40 PRO Rail 509 N&C Board 2 April 1844. Dobson attended with the plan for the site of the permanent station. For months negotiations proceeded with Newcastle Town Council, leading to the purchase of land east of the Infirmary gardens, corresponding to the west end of the present Central Station.

41 ibid. The meeting with Hudson was reported by Matthew Plummer, N&C chairman, on 7 January 1845. Harrison and George Stephenson had accompanied Hudson and they had gone into details of station arrangements.

Chapter 2

1 PRO Rail 772/71.

2 PRO Rail 772/3 N&DJ Board 8 September 1843. The same meeting approved the 3% guarantee on the Greens' Tyne Bridge, subject to its costing no more than £100,000 to construct and Newcastle Corporation giving any of their land which might be required. The Brandling Junction and other railways 'north of Darlington' were expected to participate in the bridge guarantee; its design, position and contractor were subject to the approval and supervision of Robert Stephenson.

3 Reported on 1 March 1844 in the Gateshead Observer, which stated that no such 'Yankee notion' was entertained by the railway.

4 The progress of the station was regularly reported in the Gateshead Observer, with the building illustrated and described in the issue of 22 June 1844.

5 Euston Station and the line as far as Boxmoor opened on 20 July 1837. Charles Fox was resident engineer between Euston and Camden under Robert Stephenson, the Engineer-in-Chief. An early engineering account of the line, with detailed drawings, was published at the beginning of 1838 by John Weale in 'The Public Works of Great Britain', edited by F.W. Simms (British Library). Normally Simms makes no reference to the resident engineers but in the case of Euston and the Camden engine house he goes out of his way to state that the iron roofs were erected under the direction of Fox. This suggests that Fox may have been responsible for their design; Stephenson, after all, had far more serious design problems to contend with whereas these roofs were just a further stage in the development of iron and composite iron-and-timber trusses which had been progressing in textile mills and other industrial buildings for several decades.

6 The Birmingham Curzon Street terminus, opened 9 April 1838, is described in Roscoe's Guide to the London & Birmingham Railway in terms which imply that the trainshed roof had planking below the slates.

7 The internal arrangements of Greenesfield Station are revealed in an original plan and elevation in the collection of the late Ken Hoole (Ken Hoole Study Centre, Darlington), which, together with site measurements, is the principal basis for the drawings published here.

8 The offices were completely gutted but the hotel was relatively little altered, although at some stage the first-floor windows were enlarged by dropping their cills while an extension was made to the rear.

9 PRO RAIL 527/502 is a 20 feet/inch plan of Gateshead Works in January 1865 and forms the basis for the outline plan reproduced here, which omits the large stores building which stood to the east of the former station. The engine shed was designed as a rectangular building, but its north-west corner was cut back in construction to avoid the cost or difficulty of building up ground at the steeply-sloping edge of the site. The original shed roads and (apparently 42 feet diameter) turntables proved inadequate for later express locomotives, and the shed underwent at least two reconstructions, the latest by British Railways during 1963-4. At the time of writing, portions of the original fabric survive in the now-derelict building.

10 Ken Hoole 'North Road Locomotive Works, Darlington: 1863-1966' pub. 1967.
11 F.W.D. Manders op. cit.
12 ibid.

Chapter 3

1 The most recent biography of Dobson is Tom Faulkner & Andrew Greg 'John Dobson, Newcastle Architect', pub. 1987. This largely, but not entirely, supersedes Lyall Wilkes 'John Dobson', pub. 1980.
2 Howard Colvin 'A Biographical Dictionary of British Architects, 1600-1840', 3rd edition 1995.
3 Holme Eden, at Warwick Bridge, was built for the prominent Carlisle millowner Peter Dixon, a promoter of the Newcastle & Carlisle Railway; some of Dobson's drawings for it are held in Newcastle's Laing Art Gallery.
4 Dobson's perspective for this station is held in the British Architectural Library, though wrongly catalogued as a station at Carlisle.
5 W.W. Tomlinson op. cit., pp. 292-3.
6 Andrews designed the first three terraces, including the Royal Hotel, though these are often mistakenly attributed to Dobson, whose earliest work was the somewhat-mongrel East Crescent.
7 This account is condensed from John Addyman 'T.E. Harrison, Father of the NER' in North Eastern Express Numbers 102 and 103 (1986).
8 The 1844 main line through County Durham, north of Ferryhill, was replaced in two stages. The Team Valley route from Durham to Gateshead opened to local traffic on 1 December 1868, but would not have been accessible to main-line trains until the opening of the route from Ferryhill to Durham on 15 January 1872.
9 Quoted from Brian Bailey 'George Hudson - The Rise and Fall of the Railway King', pub. Alan Sutton, 1995. Supplementing this very readable account of Hudson's career, there is A.J. Peacock's detailed biography 'George Hudson' published privately in two volumes in 1988 and 1989.
10 Reported in evidence by John Close, Hudson's secretary, to the YNM Committee of Investigation, 1849.
11 Despite some shortcomings and a number of more recent books, the best general biography currently available is L.T.C. Rolt 'George & Robert Stephenson', pub. Longmans 1960.

Chapter 4

1 Proceedings of the Newcastle Town Council 8 Jan. 1845. pp. 3-6. T.W.A. and Newcastle City Library.
2 Northumberland Railway, Plans and Sections (1844) N.C.R.O., QRU p. 63.
3 Prospectus for proposed High Level Bridge over Tyne (1839) T.W.A., 285 N.C.R.O., 309/B12.
4 Bill Fawcett, A History of the York-Scarborough Railway pp. 16-18.
5 W. W. Tomlinson, The North Eastern Railway, Its Rise and Development p. 461. Northumberland Railway supporters formally withdrew their opposition to Newcastle and Berwick on 28 June 1845.
6 Newcastle and Berwick Act 1845. Clause 26 of the Act is almost word-for-word as written by the Town Clerk of Newcastle with the significant exception that the railway was required to start within nine months instead of the six months specified by Newcastle. The reduction from the five years, agreed with Hudson, to four years for the completion was a compromise based on Gateshead's insistence on three years (Proceedings Newcastle Town Council 2 April 1845). Why Gateshead was so keen to loose its status as the northern terminus of the line from London is a mystery. The driving of the first pile for the bridge was referred to in a contemporary document as "the first nail in Gateshead's coffin".-Northumberland County Library, Morpeth.
7 Captain R. M. Laffan R.E. Notes upon the High Level Bridge at Newcastle - to be appended to Captain Laffan's report dated August 11, 1849. Handwritten document P.R.O. MT6 7/101.
8 Robert Stephenson. "Iron Bridges" Encyclopaedia Britannica (1856, pp. 586-610). p. 604. British Library.
9 R. Hodgson. Set of six coloured drawings produced in 1858-9. Institution of Civil Engineers, Library.
10 North Eastern Railway Gradient Sections 1905. Reprinted by N.E.R.A. 1996.
11 Tomlinson. op. cit. p. 320, quotes gradients of Redheugh branch as 1 in 23 but the NER gradient sections show the gradients as eased to 1 in 36 to permit locomotive working in 1905.
12 House of Lords Records Vol. 4, 1845. Evidence prior to the incorporation of the Newcastle and Berwick Railway.
13 Plans and Sections for Newcastle and Berwick Railway. N.C.R.O. QRU p. 58.
14 Original drawings, Railtrack Records Centre, Hudson House, York.
15 The largest masonry bridges in Britain are: Road, Grosvenor Bridge, Chester, span 200ft., built 1832; Rail, Ballochmyle Viaduct, Ayrshire, span 181ft., built 1848.
16 R. Stephenson. op. cit. p. 586.
17 W. A. Provis, A historical and descriptive account of the suspension bridge constructed over the Menai Strait in North Wales (1828).
18 R. W. Rennison, Civil Engineering Heritage, Northern England. p. 193.
19 Great Exhibition Catalogue 1851. p. 322. Mitchell Library, Glasgow.
20 Faustus Verantius, Machinae novea (1616). British Library.
21 European Magazine. September 1820. pp. 236-7. Letter dated 19 September 1820, written by "F.M., Bury Street". British Library.
22 R. Stephenson. op. cit. p. 603.
23 Ibid., pp. 559-600.
24 G. Drysdale Dempsey C.E. Tubular Bridges (1850) (reprinted 1970) pp. 7-10.

25 F. R. Conder (edited by J. Simmons 1983). The Men Who Built Railways, p. 141. The bridge was actually designed by the "mathematical genius" G. P. Bidder (1806-78) who succeeded Stephenson and Locke to become president of the I.C.E. 1859-61. The Gateshead Observer for 3 August 1850 describing the celebration dinner for Robert Stephenson refers to G. P. Bidder as "once famous as 'the Calculating Boy', and now an illustration of the truth, 'the child's the father of the man',". This is the only snide remark made about any guest.

26 Minutes of Evidence taken before the Commissioners appointed to inquire into the Application of Iron to Railway Structures (1849 Report). Robert Stephenson's evidence was heard on 16 March 1848 and was covered by questions 803 to 940 in the report.-I.C.E. Library and British Library.

27 Ibid. p. 339, questions 925-928.

28 G. Drysdale Dempsey. op. cit. pp. 44-6.

29 L. T. C. Rolt. Isambard Kingdom Brunel (1957 Edition), p. 327.

30 G. Drysdale Dempsey op. cit. pp.13, 103.

31 Ibid. pp. 46-132.

32 R. B. Dockray. "Description of the Camden Station of the London and North-Western Railway". Proceedings of the Institution of Civil Engineers 1849, pp. 169-170.-I.C.E. Library.

33 G. Drysdale Dempsey, op. cit. pp. 33-38.

34 1849 Report, op. cit. p. 340. Questions 937-940.

35 R. Stephenson, op. cit. p. 598.

36 P. S. A. Berridge. The Girder Bridge, pp 157-158. This book gives a very good summary of the 1849 Report.

37 Ibid. p. 41.

38 G. Drysdale Dempsey, op. cit. pp. 41-43.

39 Requirements of the Board of Trade in regard to the Opening of Railways. 1905. p. 9.

40 R. M. Laffan, op. cit.

41 T. E. Harrison "On the Tyne Docks at South Shields; and the mode adopted for Shipping Coals". Proc. I.C.E. 1859. Plate 9. Longitudinal Section of River Tyne.-Institution of Civil Engineers, Library.

42 R. M. Laffan, op. cit.

43 Newcastle and Berwick Act 1845.

44 R. M. Laffan, op. cit.

45 Original drawings, Railtrack Records Centre, York.

46 R. M. Laffan, op. cit

47 G. B. Bruce, "Description of the Royal Border Bridge over the River Tweed, on the York, Newcastle and Berwick Railway". Proc. I.C.E. 1851. pp. 233-7.-Institution of Civil Engineers, Library.

48 Ibid., p. 237.

49 Ibid., p. 235.

50 Three original drawings in Railtrack Records Centre and Tyne and Wear Archives give different depths from low water level to the bedrock at No. 5 pier. Two state 60ft. and one 50ft. but from the size of piles used the smaller dimension seems correct.

51 R. M. Laffan, op. cit

52 R. Stephenson, op. cit. p. 603. This bridge was replaced many years ago by a mundane plate girder bridge but a similar structure by G. Stephenson and T. Gooch at Gauxholme still remains. Grid Ref. SD 931233.

53 Whishaw's Railways of Great Britain & Ireland (1969 reprint), p. 225.

54 Gateshead Observer, 3 August 1850. p. 6. Gateshead M.B.C. Library, Local Studies.

55 Original drawings in Railtrack Records Centre, York.

56 R. Stephenson, op. cit. p. 605.

57 Ibid.

58 1849 Report, p. 332, question 807. Robert Stepenson refers to an 1847 paper "... by Professor Johnson, in which he endeavoured to trace the peculiarities of the iron in different parts of the country to a small admixture of phosphorus, I think, in Welch (sic) iron, and a small portion of manganese in the Yorkshire iron".

59 Ibid. p. 333, question 824.

60 Ibid. p. 333, question 814.

61 Ibid. Appendix 4.

62 Robert Stephenson, op. cit. p. 605.

63 Gateshead Observer, 3 August, 1850. p. 6.

64 The Illustrated London News, 9 September 1848, p. 149.-National Railway Museum, Library, York.

65 Gateshead Observer, 27 March 1847.

66 Newcastle and Berwick Board minutes, P.R.O.

67 Gateshead Observer, 3 August 1850, p. 6.

68 Original drawings in Railtrack Records Centre, Hudson House, York.

69 Gateshead Observer, 25 July 1846, p. 1.

70 Ibid.

71 Newcastle and Berwick Board minutes, 17 August 1846. P.R.O.

72 High Level Bridge, Iron Work Contract, Specification (July 1846). P.R.O. Rail 772/34, p. 5.

73 Gateshead Observer, 14 November 1846.

74 Ibid. 14 August 1846, p. 3.

75 Ibid. 16 January 1847, p. 3.

76 Ibid. 27 March 1847, p. 3.

77 Newcastle Journal, 23 March, 1847

78 Ibid. 12 June 1847 and 26 June 1847.

79 R. Stephenson, op. cit. p. 605. Also Gateshead Observer, 16 January 1847.

80 R. M. Laffan, op. cit.

81 Ibid. also R. Stephenson, op. cit. p. 604.

82   Gateshead Observer, 3 August 1850. p. 6.

83   R. A. Cook and K. Hoole, North Eastern Railway Historical Maps, p. 25.

84   Gateshead Observer, 21 August 1847, p. 2.

85   The Illustrated London News, 9 September 1848, p. 149. N.R.M. Library, York.

86   Gateshead Observer, 3 August, 1850. p. 6.

87   Original drawings Railtrack Records Centre, York, also R. M. Laffan op. cit.

88   R. Stephenson, op. cit. p. 604.

89   Gateshead Observer, 3 August 1850. p. 6.

90   R. M. Laffan, op. cit.

91   R. Stephenson, op. cit. p. 604.

92   T. E. Harrison, op. cit. p. 515.

93   Letter from T. E. Harrison to John Close (secretary to the Newcastle and Berwick) dated 17 April 1846. P.R.O.
     Rail 772/96.

94   S. Smiles, George and Robert Stephenson (1871) p. 316.

95   G. B. Bruce, op. cit. pp. 221-225.

96   Gateshead Observer, 3 October 1846, p. 2.

97   G. B. Bruce, op. cit. p. 221.

98   Gateshead Observer, 10 October, 1846, p. 2.

99   R. Stephenson, op. cit. p. 604.

100 Ibid. p. 604.

101 S. Smiles, Lives of Engineers (1887) p. 313. British Library.

102 R. M. Laffan, op. cit.

103 Original drawings, Railtrack Records Centre, York.

104 C. F. Bengough. "High-Level Bridge, Newcastle-upon-Tyne: Underpinning and Repair of Foundations of River
     Piers". Proc. I.C.E. 1926, p. 177.-Institution of Civil Engineers, Library.

105 R. Stephenson, op. cit. pp. 604-605.

106 1849 Report, op. cit. letter, p. 390.

107 Gateshead Observer, 24 July 1847, p. 2.

108 Ibid. 26 February 1848, p. 3. The "leaky tub" referred to was the original Brandling Junction Railway bridge over
     West Street.

109 Ibid. 20 May 1848, p. 3.

110 Ibid. 26 June 1847, p. 3.

111 Ibid. 9 June, 1849, p. 2.

112 Ibid. 25 August 1849, p. 2.

113 Ibid. 1 September 1849, p. 3.

114 Ibid. 9 June 1849, p. 2, 3 August 1850, p. 6.

115 Ibid. 18 August 1849, p. 3.

116 The Illustrated London News, 6 October 1849, p. 233.

117 Gateshead Observer, 21 March 1846, p. 3.

118 R. Stephenson, op. cit. p. 605.

119 Gateshead Observer, 16 February 1850, p. 5.

120 Ibid. 1 February 1851, p. 5.

121 R. Stephenson, op. cit. p. 605. Also R. M. Laffan, op. cit.

122 The Britannia Bridge was to cost £600,000 and it is of interest to note that Southwark Bridge (Road) cost
     £800,000 in 1819.

123 Newcastle and Berwick Act 1845, clause 30.

124 North Eastern Railway printed notice.

125 The North-eastern (sic) Railway Company's Act, 1869, clauses 24-30.

126 Newcastle Journal, 13 June 1931.

127 LNER and Newcastle and Gateshead Corporations agreement for the transfer of tolls payable in respect of the
     High Level Bridge at Newcastle-upon-Tyne and for their abolition. Agreement No. 5201 dated 10 May 1937,
     signed by an assistant secretary for the LNER, and the Mayors and Town Clerks of Newcastle and Gateshead. F.
     W. D. Manders, A History of Gateshead, p. 123, states £250,000 for compensation against the £160,000 recorded
     in the Agreement and £22,000 per annum which was only raised prior to the Tyne Bridge opening in 1928. The
     tolls were probably removed on 12 May 1937, King George VI's Coronation Day.

128 K. Hoole, Rail Centres: Newcastle, p. 28.

129 N.E.R. Gradient Sections 1905. Extra mileage was also permitted over Scotswood railway bridge.

130 LNER, On Either Side, pp. 23-24.

131 Ken Hoole, op. cit. p. 28.

132 Ibid. p. 75.

133 Ibid. p. 26.

134 Bill Fawcett, "Sir John Wolfe Barry and the Newcastle Traffic Problem" The North Eastern Express February
     1994, p. 104, based on PRO RAIL 527/1039.

135 Ibid. pp. 103-106.

136 F. W. Davis and C. R. S. Kirkpatrick "The King Edward VII Bridge, Newcastle-on-Tyne". Proc. I.C.E. 1907-8,
     pp. 158-187.

137 K. Hoole, The North Eastern Electrics: The History of the Tyneside Electric Passenger Services (1904-1967), pp.
     4, 8, 64-68, 74, 75.

138 N.E.R. drawing dated 1919.

139 Information supplied independently by two former B.R. bridge engineers. According to P. W. Elliston (Chap. 7) the tracks over the bridge were also considered for removal in 1969 when the cast manganese diamonds were due for renewal (see Chapter 7).

140 W. R. Preston, "Repair and maintenance of listed cast and wrought iron bridges". Conservation of engineering structures. Thomas Telford, London, 1989, p. 28.

141 S. Middlebrook. Newcastle Upon Tyne, p. 191.

142 The Illustrated London News, 9 September 1848, p. 149.

143 R. Stephenson, op. cit. p. 604.

144 Proceeding of the Newcastle Town Council, 3 September 1879. The tolls for the Redheugh Bridge for 1878 were £4,000.

145 Ibid. 1925.

146 Gateshead Observer, 30 June 1866, p. 3.

147 NER memoranda dated 8 April 1910 dictated by Mr. J. Simpkin on his retirement.

148 Original drawing in Railtrack Records Centre, York.

149 C. F. Bengough (see 104) op. cit. pp. 173-175.

150 Original drawing in Railtrack Records Centre, York, shows measurements taken with theodolite from south end of swing-bridge.

151 C. F. Bengough, op. cit. pp. 175-195.

152 NER memoranda, op. cit.

153 Ibid.

154 Original drawings in Railtrack Records Centre, York. A coloured drawing gives dates for completion of each item of work.

155 Agreement 10 May 1937, op. cit.

156 B.R. memorandum, dated 20 January 1969.

157 Original drawings in Railtrack Record Centre, York.

158 A. H. Jenkins, a later regional bridge engineer, condemned the ballasting as "monstrous folly" in a lecture in the early 1960s.

159 Interim report to B.R. dated January 1968.

160 W. R. Preston, op. cit. p. 21.

161 Ibid. pp. 22-26.

162 Ibid, pp. 18, 28.

163 Ibid, p. 28.

164 Gateshead Observer, 23 July 1859, p. 5.

165 Information from former B.R. bridge engineer based on samples analysed by former B.R. Research Department at Derby.

166 The Journal, Statutory Notice, February 1999.

167 R. M. Laffan, op. cit. gave theoretical stresses in the arch ribs of 1.83 tons per sq. in. and in the chains of 6.48 tons per sq. in. By the time of his death in 1882 Laffan had become Lt. Gen. Sir Robert Laffan.

168 LNER memorandum dated 7 October 1935 "Analysis of original and present day relationship of the Railway and Roadway Loading and Costs".

169 W. R. Preston, op. cit. p. 21.

Chapter 5

1 PRO MT6 Report of Captain Coddington, 22 February 1847.

2 Newcastle Journal 27 February 1847.

3 PRO Rail 509 Newcastle & Carlisle Railway Board 1 June 1846. Dobson showed the directors his drawings and was told to find out from the Managing Committee the arrangements needed for the company's offices so that he could make a plan and have the building proceed without further delay.

4 PRO Rail 772/3 Newcastle & Darlington Junction Railway Board 18 August 1846 - the working drawings would be the immediate preliminary to advertising for tenders to construct the station.

5 Newcastle Journal 30 January 1847. In 1835 the N&C had purchased land from Newcastle Corporation for a terminus at the Spital. When Central Station was determined on an exchange of lands was agreed, with the Council then reselling part of the Spital site to Hudson's companies but Alderman Dunn felt that the N&C, who were compensated for having money tied up in an unproductive property, were profiting at the expense of the council and the upshot was a Chancery suit which benefited no-one.

6 ibid. 16 January 1847 contained the first advertisement.

7 ibid. 14 August 1847. There is no record of the principal contract in the company's minutes, though later ones for plastering and the trainshed are recorded. The Journal gives the contractors as MacKay & Reed, however they are always referred to in minutes and reports as MacKay & Blackstock and were already operating thus as contractors on the Newcastle & Berwick. The first report of the YNB Committee of Investigation (PRO Rail 772/15) quotes a figure of £92,097.

8 Hudson had promoted the Team Valley line from Durham to Gateshead as a more direct main line, while the Leeds & Thirsk Railway were pursuing a rival scheme as part of their (unsuccessful) strategy to form an independent route between Yorkshire and Tyneside. In June 1847 Parliament decided in favour of Hudson, but construction was abandoned as a YNB economy. The line was eventually built by the North Eastern Railway, opening to passengers on 1 December 1868, and forms the present main line.

9 Newcastle Journal 18 September 1847.

10 Some of Dobson's certificates for payments to MacKay & Blackstock survive in the PRO. Number 6, covering 30 July to 4 September, records the first purchases of walling stone, 2,900 cubic feet at 10d per cubic foot for use above ground in the north and south walls of the office building.

11 YNB Board 13 February 1849. Mr. MacBeath and Mr. Carstairs attended on behalf of the contractors.

12 ibid. 10 April 1849: decision to advertise for the ironwork, and on 16 April, during the last fortnight of Hudson's chairmanship, approval of Dobson's revised design for the roof, bringing the cost down from £12,000 to £10,000. The ironwork contract was not minuted but Gibson's was, on 28 May, for £2,552-11-9.

13 ibid. 23 May 1849: 'The committee of investigation having recommended the directors to continue their interdict against proceeding with the arcade, portico or hotel' this was to be communicated to Dobson who was to be instructed 'to comply with it strictly'.

14 ibid. 25 January 1850 There is no record in the minutes of Newcastle Town Council that a contribution was ever discussed there.

15 ibid. 25 January 1850. These were the booking office, parcels office, waiting rooms and offices above.

16 The dinner was principally to celebrate Stephenson's achievements at the Britannia and High Level Bridges, which were portrayed along with the Royal Border Bridge on huge banners above the heads of the diners. It was extensively reported, including Newcastle Journal 3 August 1850 and Illustrated London News 10 August 1850.

17 A full account of the opening day appears in Newcastle Journal 31 August 1850.

18 Newcastle Journal 6 September 1851: 'the front of the Central Railway station has been at length thrown open, and the mass of scaffolding, stones and mortar which obstructed the view removed. the building has a noble appearance, and reflects the highest degree of credit upon the architect Mr. Dobson; but the elevation would, no doubt, be greatly improved by the portico'.

19 TWA GU/BS/12 contains details of the Barber Surgeons relocation. The agreement to sell the old hall was signed on 15 September 1847 and, as with the Bricklayers, the YNB was to find a site and build a new hall. It did neither, but in 1850 agreed to pay the Barber-Surgeons £845 in lieu of a site and £1,760 in lieu of building the hall.

20 Newcastle Town Council 13 June and 12 September 1838. Notices to dispossess tenants were served about the end of July. On 3 July 1839 the Council approved the building of a link into Forth Street and the adoption of uniform building elevations for the new (Neville) street.

21 ibid. 9 September 1846

22 PRO Rail 772/1 YNB Committee of Management 15 March 1848.

23 PRO Rail 527 NER Locomotive Committee 22 April 1864 minute 6795.

24 The roof recladding is detailed in contract drawings dated 8 February 1876 and held in Railtrack's York Record Centre - ref. 102/19-23.

25 Dobson's presidential address to the first quarterly meeting of the Northern Architectural Association, 19 April 1859, reprinted in Lyall Wilkes, op. cit. Dobson recalled that cutting curved plates out of sheets increased 'the expense so much that at one time I did not find myself justified in introducing them'.

26 The Official Illustrated Catalogue of the Great Exhibition of 1851 (p. 323) lists the following exhibits by Dobson in Class 7: Model of the roof over the passenger shed of the station; model of the original design for the portico and arcades; model of the rolling machine 'designed by Mr. Thomas Charlton, used in rolling iron for the circular principals of the passenger-shed roof'. Dobson also exhibited a model of the roof he had recently designed for Smith's Shipyard at St. Peter's, which was extensively glazed and may have been related to Central Station.

27 R.S. Fitzgerald 'Liverpool Road Station, Manchester', pub. 1980.

28 Bill Fawcett 'Yorkshire's Earliest Railway Stations' in Yorkshire Philosophical Society Annual Report for 1997.

29 Proc. ICE 4 June 1844 'Description of the Iron Shed at the London Terminus of the Eastern Counties Railway' by William Evill, junior.

30 Described in numerous books, including P. Lavedan 'French Architecture', Penguin, 1956.

31 G.F. Chadwick 'Paxton and the Great Stove' in Architectural History, Journal of the Society of Architectural Historians of Great Britain, vol. 4 (1961).

32 Patent 10,143 of 15 April 1844 granted to Thomas Vernon, shipbuilder, and James Kennedy, engineer, of Bury, Curtis & Kennedy.

33 A good description is found in J. Hix 'The Glasshouse' Phaidon 1996.

34 Patent 11,496 for this form of roof construction, applied to railway stations, was secured by Turner on 15 December 1846. It shows cast deck-beams and fabricated I-beams as alternative forms of principal in a crescent truss.

35 R. Turner 'Description of the Iron Roof over the Railway Station, Lime-Street, Liverpool' in Proc. ICE. 19 February 1850, p.204.

36 G. Biddle 'Great Railway Stations of Britain', pub. 1986.

37 Later replaced by iron ribs. An account is given by G. Biddle op. cit.

38 Thompson began his association with railways on the North Midland Railway, where he was employed on the staff of the company, on Stephenson's recommendation, to design stations and other buildings. Once construction was over he was discharged. Thus Thompson may be the first full-time railway architect but, unlike Prosser, not in a permanent post.

39 Hudson's lease of the N&C ran from 1 July 1848 and was only surrendered at the end of 1849. Under it, Harrison came in as Engineer-in-Chief, with Peter Tate remaining engineer. James Allport, YNB general manager, oversaw finance and ensured that profits were directed to the YNB rather than Hudson personally.

40 NER Locomotive Committee 10 October 1856 and PRO Rail 527/1303 NER Accounts Summary Book: work was commissioned in October 1856 and completed by May 1857.

41 The two arrival platform sheds at Chester were basically continued forward by a further span to create covered cab drives flanking the forecourt of the main entrance.

42 Cambridge Station was reported in the Railway Chronicle 2 August 1845.

43 Royal Commission on the Historical Monuments of England, Inventory of the City of Cambridge, 1959, citing Cambridge Chronicle 21 November 1863.

44 Civil Engineer & Architect's Journal September 1845, p. 295.

45 N&C Board: on 24 December 1849 Dobson attended with the plans for the offices as revised for the YNB but the N&C directors determined to press for completion of the original design; the final revised scheme with the modified portico was shown to them on 6 March.

46 Semi-circular windows, usually with a tripartite glazing division, long popular in neo-classical and Palladian architecture and derived from the Roman Baths of Diocletian. They are also referred to here as lunettes.

47 Various portico designs exist in the Dobson collection of the Laing Art Gallery, Newcastle.

48 Illustrated London News 10 August 1850. Quite apart from a general clumsiness, the engraver has reduced the number of arches along the front from 7 to 6.

49 PRO Rail 527/724 NER Book of Agreements Volume 2 records a formal agreement made on 6 June 1862, clause 2 of which bound the NER to complete the portico before the end of 1863; another clause specified the increased provision of third-class carriages on main-line trains.

50 The set of elevations and sections for the portico in the Laing Art Gallery, Newcastle, bears the date September 1861. One of the drawings carries Dobson's office stamp, which appears to have been lost from the others when ragged edges were trimmed. Before being presented to the Laing, they were in the collection of working drawings in the Railway Architect's Office, York. Until the insertion of the present offices, the portico had a pitched roof running lengthwise instead of the transverse spans shown in these drawings.

51 PRO Rail 527 NER Locomotive Committee: 21 November 1862 minute 5952 records the letting of the contract for the portico, exclusive of the roof, to Scott & Reed for £5,428; the roof was let on 24 June 1863, minute 6191, to Waite & Howard for £1,449-13-0; the final cost was reported on 12 February 1864, minute 6677, as £7,223-0-9.

52 Discussion in Newcastle Town Council.

53 Newcastle Journal 15 June 1850. Staite had first exhibited his lights in London in 1848. A display at Sunderland Harbour, also a Hudson's enterprise, had been reported on 8 June. For the Stephenson banquet a large perforated gas tube was used to shed light from a high level.

54 PRO Rail 772/52, compiled by John & Benjamin Green, details payments made to contractors for buildings on the N&B. Payments for the temporary station at Manors began in October 1847.

55 Newcastle Journal 16 October 1847.

56 The contract for Trafalgar Goods Station was let by the YNB Committee of Management (PRO Rail 772/1) to Richard Cail on 18 May 1848 for £20,500; the same meeting let the contract for Green's 'Corn Loft' to Rush & Lawton for £13,500. Dobson referred to the foundation problems in his address to the Northern Architectural Association, Lyall Wilkes op. cit.

57 It had a very fine series of fully-glazed verandah platform roofs, a portion of which, along with the cupola from its booking office, has been erected at the Marsden Rattler public house on the South Shields seafront.

58 Manors Station was largely rebuilt in 1886-7 in connection with the quadrupling of the tracks between Manors and Heaton Junction, though Dobson's building was retained at that stage. This portion became known as Manors East on the opening of the new North platforms on the link line to Jesmond in 1909. A full account of Manors Station is given in Bill Fawcett 'Manors Station' in North Eastern Express vol. 25 no. 102 (1986).

59 A more detailed account of the original Forth Goods Station and its translation to Central Station is given in Bill Fawcett 'Newcastle Central Carriage Shed' in North Eastern Express vol. 26 no. 109, 1987.

Chapter 6

1 PRO Rail 772/53 contains papers regarding Jeffery's offer to lease the hotel, made in December 1851, and proposals for the new lease in 1863.

2 PRO Rail 527 NER Locomotive Committee 12 May 1854 indicates that the refreshment rooms were still incomplete.

3 ibid. 7 December 1860 and 13 September 1861.

4 ibid. 27 February 1863   The new building at the Newcastle hotel to be insured for £5,000.

5 PRO Rail 509/69 Volume of correspondence regarding the amalgamation. The Act authorising it received the Royal Assent on 17 July 1862.

6 Proc. ICE 13 February 1866 - Contribution by T.E. Harrison to the discussion on 'On the Design and Arrangement of Railway Stations etc' by W. Humber. Harrison said that the new platforms would be 3 feet high, but later drawings clearly show them to be 2 feet 8 inches above rail level. Further raising has been achieved by sloping the concourse surface gradually up from the station offices so as not to interfere with door cill levels.

7 PRO Rail 527 NER Locomotive Committee 10 November 1865 minute 7831 approved the work, and on 7 December 1866 John Bourne, the Northern Division Engineer, reported it had cost £4,878-8-8 to lower the lines, widen platforms and provide a new one.

8 Board of Trade Accident Reports (NRM). Colonel C.S. Hutchinson reporting 20 April 1871 on an accident on 5 April 1871. A train from Tynemouth hit the buffers and two passengers were bruised. The gradient was 1/177.

9 W. W. Tomlinson op. cit. quotes 1871 and this is consistent with the track remodelling and signalling work known to have been carried out at that time.

10 Forth Banks ran between the station and the Infirmary; this alignment is now a footpath, the road having been diverted to the opposite side of the Infirmary site.

11 PRO Rail 527 NER Locomotive Committee 27 June 1873 - Alfred Harrison, then Northern Division Engineer, had the uncomfortable task of explaining why the final cost of £5,521-13-0, which seems quite a good bargain for the work done, was more than twice the authorised estimate.

12 ibid. 19 June 1863.

13 ibid. 26 February 1875. The delay arose from the attitude of Newcastle Corporation, who, though normally helpful to the NER, sought unreasonable improvements to New Bridge Street as the price of their assent to a link originally proposed in 1874.

14 PRO Rail 527/726: NER Agreements Book contains an agreement of 2 May 1883 with Newcastle Corporation showing the road diversions to accommodate the east end widening, but with no incursion onto the original alignment of Forth Street though that road was to be extended east from Orchard Street to Clavering Place at the expense of the railway. Some enlargement could have been made on to the sites of the original engine sheds.

15 Newcastle City Council: Councillor Youll speaking at the meeting on 4 April 1883 which agreed to support the NER Bill in Parliament.

16 Table IX of the Report of the Medical Officer of Health presented by the Sanitary Committee to Newcastle City Council on 5 February 1890.

17 TWA 459/366-369 Records of the Trustees of the Blessed Virgin Mary Hospital dealing with the land sale.

18 PRO Rail 527 NER Way & Works Committee 17 February 1887 minute 3337 contains approval of the scheme at £600 and a draft agreement with Newcastle Corporation. TWA holds a plan with details of the structure, portions of which had to be demountable to enable 'engines and large boilers' to get in and out of Stephenson's South Street Works.

19 The platform was opened for use by visitors to the Mining, Engineering & Industrial Exhibition in May 1887; a Board of Trade inspection report is filed in PRO MT6 433/13 and explains that a temporary signalbox was provided to control passenger train movements.

20 PRO Rail 527 NER Way & Works Committee 20 September 1888 minute 4431: the contract for the substructure was let to Henderson, Matthew & Co. of Edinburgh at £37,471-14-1, but they made slow progress and the work was relet to Walter Scott & Co. of Newcastle in August 1889 for £45,397 less the value of any work completed by Henderson's. Minute 4353: the hotel contract was let to Walter Scott at £51,000 - seven times the cost of the 1863 building during an era of low inflation.

21 PRO Rail 527/94 and 527/95: NER Hotels Committee 1877-1911 and 1911-1922.

22 British Architect 10 November 1893.

23 PRO Rail 527/94: the NER Hotels Committee accepted estimates on 5 January 1893 of £2,346 for the refreshment room and £315 for the adjoining attendant's room.

24 PRO Rail 527 NER Way & Works Committee 5 February 1891. Minute 6105 referred to a revised plan for the station extensions, by Charles Harrison and William Bell, with 2 footbridges (presumably one for passengers and one for parcels) instead of an earlier scheme for two subways. Contracts were let to Walter Scott and to W.B. Wilkinson & Co. on the basis of schedules of prices.

25 ibid. 21 January 1892 minute 6832. Contracts were let for individual trades in the extensions to the trainshed roof and some office alterations. The total came to £60,243-19-0, of which the Tees Side Iron & Engine Works Co. accounted for £38,101-17-1 in 'ironfounders' and smiths' work', while J.H. Shouksmith of York, a common NER contractor for glazing and lead work, took £7,991-4-8.

26 PRO MT6 664/4 contains Major General Hutchinson's inspection reports on the extensions. A portion was inspected in January 1893, when two of the new signal cabins - numbers 1 and 4 - were brought into use. The entire layout was inspected in May 1894, although the widened lines to Manors were not yet complete. Very unusually, since he was principally concerned with the safety of the track layout and signalling, Hutchinson requested drawings of the trainshed roof extensions.

27 E.M. Bywell 'Notable Railway Stations - Newcastle Central' in Railway Magazine vol. VIII, 1901.

28 ibid

29 After a closure of some months, while conversion took place, the first electric tram services began in December 1901.

30 Several accounts of the electrification have been written, but one of the most attractive remains Ken Hoole's 'The North Eastern Electrics', published by Oakwood Press in 1961 when the full system, including the Riverside Branch and the line down to Newcastle Quayside, was still in operation.

31 Detailed figures are given in Hoole op. cit.

32 PRO Rail 527/48 NER Way & Works Committee. The contract for the new platform roofing at the west end, together with additional passenger facilities, was not let until 26 July 1906, the builder being Bertram Bolam of Birtley at a price of £15,000.

33 TWA T186/A2202 contains plans for this and later planning applications to Newcastle Corporation in respect of the hotel, down to 1955. The 1923 extension is one of very few schemes by the NER's last Chief Architect, Stephen Wilkinson, who took over in 1922 but was soon made redundant by LNER economies.

34 Smith was the job architect preparing the drawings, though under Charles Bridgen, head of the office.

35 An agreement was made on 31 December 1930 between the LNER and the Post Office, which was building a new sorting office in Forth Street (linked by subway to the station). The accompanying plans show a broad strip of LNER property, 55 feet wide at the crossing of South Street, on the south side of Forth Street. Some was sold to the GPO on condition that any buildings erected on it were of a temporary nature, the LNER reserving a right of repurchase within 21 years if required for railway purposes. Thus this land was still available to them in 1947. Another such property was Clavering House, at the east end of Forth Street, which for many years housed the railway's District Estate Surveyor.

36 Railtrack York Record Centre reference Reel 130, Frame 187.

37 The work was carried out under the direction of Arthur Dean as Chief Civil Engineer to the North Eastern Region but, very unusually, an outside firm of architects, S.W. Milburn & Partners of Sunderland, was called in.

38 This downgrading of the main line was recommended in Beeching's second report, 'The Development of the Major Railway Trunk Routes', published in 1965.

Chapter 7: Track

1 J. F. Addyman, "Civil Engineering" North Eastern Record Vol. 1, p. 36.

2 W. W. Tomlinson, The North Eastern Railway - Its Rise and Development, p. 648.

3 J. F. Addyman, op. cit. p. 36.
4 Thomas Ridley, "Permanent Way Renewals" Journal of the Permanent Way Institution 1914, pp. 83-84.
5 British Rail, Eastern Region, Permanent Way drawing 70-YP-1.
6 T. Ridley, op. cit. p. 84.
7 Ibid.
8 D. H. Coombs (editor) British Railway Track (1971) p. 25.
9 B. P. Fletcher, "The Renewal of Crossings at the East End of Central Station, Newcastle-upon-Tyne", Proceeding of the Institution of Civil Engineers, 1915, p. 1.
10 Ibid., pp. 5-9.
11 P. W. Elliston, "Newcastle East End Diamonds", Civil Engineering Technician, August 1974, pp. 20-24.
12 Ibid. p. 21.

Chapter 7: Signalling - Bibliography

NER Magazine and its successors 1911-1999.
Railway Magazine 1901.
The Railway Engineer 1882, 1898.
NER Appendix to Working Timetable 1873, 1874, 1889, 1892, 1898, 1904, 1911, 1918, 1922.
NER Signalling Alterations Circular 1887.
NER Operating Circulars 1909.
LNER Appendix to Working Timetable 1931, 1947.
LNER/BR Weekly and special programmes of signalling alterations 1928-1991.
Electro-Pneumatic Signalling, The Westinghouse Brake and Signalling Co.
Board of Trade Accident and Inspection Reports 1865-1898.
NER Minutes of Locomotive Committee 1854 and 1858.
NER Board Minutes 1854 and 1855.
W. W. Tomlinson, *The North Eastern Railway - Its Rise and Development*.
North Eastern Record Vol. 1 (1988) Chapter 3.
Philip Burtt *Control on the Railways* (1926).
Tweedie & Lascelles *Modern Railway Signalling* (1925).

Index

Newcastle
City Council

and

Gateshead

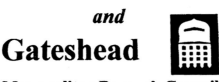

Metropolitan Borough Council

And the following Societies have supported this publication

NEWCASTLE & DISTRICT MODEL RAILWAY SOCIETY

Founded in 1970, the Society caters for railway modellers on Tyneside in all popular scales from 'Z' to gauge '0' in constructive and friendly surroundings, meeting twice weekly (Mondays and Thursdays, 7 pm to 10 pm) in their club room at 'Clyde House', 18 Westmorland Road, Newcastle, five minutes walk from Central Station. Well known for their fine North Eastern Railway layouts built over many years, the Society now hosts two well-publicised model railway exhibitions each year.

THE NORTH EASTERN RAILWAY ASSOCIATION

Formed in 1961, the NERA caters for all interested in the North Eastern Railway and Hull & Barnsley Railway, from their early history to the present day. Interests cover all aspects of operations for both the general enthusiast and model maker. With over 600 members, meetings are held throughout the year at centres such as York, Darlington, Hull and London. Outdoor visits, walks and tours are also arranged. A newsletter and a quarterly journal - *The North Eastern Express* - are issued to members. The NERA markets facsimiles of NER documents, including diagram books and station track plans, and has experts available to advise members with queries. The Association's extensive library of books, photographs, documents and drawings is held at North Road Museum in Darlington.

THE RAILWAY CORRESPONDENCE AND TRAVEL SOCIETY

This leading society was founded in 1928. With a membership of nearly 4,000 world wide, monthly meetings are held in 27 centres around the country and visits to places of railway interest take place throughout the year. High-quality publications (with members' discount on new books for a limited period) include the much-acclaimed locomotive histories of the LNER, with work now proceeding on the LMS and BR Standard Locomotive histories. Members have access to a large Society library and a photographic portfolio. Each member receives a copy of the *Railway Observer*, produced every month since its introduction in 1932 and containing the latest locomotive transfers and news of the British railway system, as well as overseas railways, urban rail systems, preserved lines and museums, etc.

THE ROBERT STEPHENSON TRUST

Robert Stephenson & Company was formed on 23rd June, 1823 and erected the first purpose-built locomotive factory in the world at South Street, Newcastle. It was the first company to export a locomotive to France and the USA, in 1828, and then to Germany, Australia, Egypt and other countries. The firm could not maintain a monopoly forever and within 20 years other locomotive works all over the world were building Stephenson type locomotives. The company also produced marine engines and bridges and at the time of Robert's death in 1859 was the largest employer on Tyneside. The Robert Stephenson Trust hopes to use the historic site for exhibitions and training

THE STEPHENSON LOCOMOTIVE SOCIETY

Founded in 1909, the Society's aims - to further appreciation of and interest in railways - remain as valid today as all those years ago. The SLS has national and local libraries, produces books, has a large photographic collection and has been active in the preservation and naming of locomotives. Among many local centres is that in Newcastle, which meets Friday evenings, as advertised, from September to May, in the Mining Institute, Neville Hall, Westgate Road at 7.00 for 7.15 p.m. Visitors are most welcome. Outdoor visits are organised during the summer months..

THE TYNE INDUSTRIAL ARCHAEOLOGY GROUP

TIAG exists to further interest and participation in the industrial archaeology of primarily, but certainly not exclusively, Tyneside. From September to April meetings are held on the fourth Thursday of each month (in December usually the second Thursday) at Gateshead's Civic Centre from 7.15 to 9 p.m. Visitors are very welcome.